THE OAK

THE OAK

Ralph Whitlock

Illustrations by Robert Morton

London
GEORGE ALLEN & UNWIN
Boston   Sydney

George Allen & Unwin (Publishers) Ltd,
40 Museum Street, London WC1A 1LU, UK

George Allen & Unwin (Publishers) Ltd,
Park Lane, Hemel Hempstead, Herts HP2 4TE, UK

Allen & Unwin Inc.,
Fifty Cross Street, Winchester, Mass 01890, USA

George Allen & Unwin Australia Pty Ltd,
8 Napier Street, North Sydney, NSW 2060, Australia

First published in 1985

British Library Cataloguing in Publication Data

Whitlock, Ralph
The oak.
1. Oak
I. Title
583'.976   QK495.F14
ISBN 0-04-635014-4

Set in 11 on 13 point Palatino by Computape (Pickering) Ltd,
North Yorkshire
and printed in Great Britain
by Butler & Tanner Ltd, Frome and London

CONTENTS

To the memory of Lady Ann Colman,
whose love of forest trees matched my own

1

THE CHETHAM OAK

THE CHETHAM OAK, or, to give it its full title, The Gospel Oak of Chetham, is a giant in decline. Like an old man whose stature shrinks as the cartilage pads between his vertebrae shrivel, the great oak has lost some of its height. Its topmost branches protrude, bare and decaying, above the leafy canopy, as though, after functioning for the best part of 800 years, the effort to supply them with food from the soil far below has become too much for the hydraulic system that sustains the life of the tree.

The oak can still, however, boast impressive dimensions. At 70 feet, it towers like a hoary patriarch above the juvenile trees grouped at a respectful distance around it. The diameter of its canopy spread, 240 feet, ensures it a surface territory of 45,216 square feet from which to draw its nourishment. Within that domain no other tree or shrub dares to intrude or compete.

The oak stands in a forest glade. Beyond the perimeter of the area it claims for its own, other trees crowd in. Young oaks, growing at forty to the acre, are dominant there, but a scattering of beech, birch, sycamore, ash and maple has also colonised this mixed deciduous wood. Beneath them a vigorous undergrowth of hazel thrives, while at the woodland margins buckthorn, blackthorn, spindle and hawthorn have secured a foothold. The parasitic honeysuckle and traveller's joy festoon themselves around every available support.

None of this exuberant jungle affects the old oak. Its only concession to undergrowth is a tangle of bracken and bramble which timidly encroaches along the western perimeter. That and the ivy which, clinging close to its great bole, acts as a kind of thermal underwear to the ancient tree. Otherwise, beneath its great horizontal arms grow only coarse grasses, herbs and lowly flowers. All of which is in keeping with the oak's status as monarch of the forest.

Not that much forest remains of its former kingdom. Only a coppice of some thirty or so acres of deciduous trees survives, though beyond them extend many hundreds of acres of regimented conifers. To the oak these latter are as alien as the speeding cars on the motorway, two fields away. When the oak was in its prime the ancestors of the upstart conifers were clinging to mountainsides in British Columbia and Oregon.

The coppice, together with the oak, is preserved as a nature reserve. It has been reprieved as a habitat of hawfinches and hobbies (though everyone is highly secretive about the latter), of the magnificent purple emperor butterfly and of the equally rare fly, butterfly and bee orchids. The oak itself is, of course, a factor in its survival. In the present climate of public opinion, no one would dare to advocate the felling of the Chetham Gospel Oak.

The clearing over which the oak presides lies just within the precincts of the coppice. A screen of lesser trees conceals all except its topmost branches from the motorway traffic. Anyone climbing to those lofty branches would enjoy a panoramic view, in one direction, of a countryside of fields, hedges, lanes, farms and villages, and, in the other, of the dark, sinister parade of firs and pines.

When the oak was a sapling the scene was very different. From horizon to far horizon nothing but trees was then visible, except for a few wispy smoke-columns which betrayed the presence of human settlement. Kites soared overhead, and the deer which grazed in the clearings were the noble red deer, not the latter-day fallow and roe. There were still wolves in the forest to cull the deer herds, and even a few surviving bears which curled up for the winter in caves now long since vanished. Those were the days when, proverbially, a squirrel could travel right across England, from sea to sea, without ever once descending from the tree-tops.

Before the great oak was even an acorn, the people whose settlements were marked by the spiralling blue smoke spoke a Celtic language. Several invasions later their place was taken by Anglo-Saxons – rough, aggressive fellows who had penetrated the country by way of the rivers and had then followed ancient tracks into the heart of the forest. The forest. When they heard the Celts whom they had enslaved talking about the forest the word used was 'chet'. In Celtic it meant simply 'forest', but the newcomers thought it was a proper name, so they called the great forest 'Chet Forest' or 'Chetwood'. The settlement nearest the great oak – or, rather, where the great oak would stand – they called 'Chetham', – 'the home in the forest'. And so it is known to this day.

The name 'Gospel Oak' belongs to a much later period. It has its origins in a time, in the Middle Ages, when the forest had been parcelled out among the English parishes. The boundaries of three of them met near the oak, which served as a useful landmark. Once a year, at Rogationtide, the villagers of Chetham were accustomed to walk in procession, led by the parish priest, around the parish boundaries. At points the company halted to hear a reading from the scripture, and the Chetham Oak was naturally one of those stations. Then an unfortunate lad

3

was up-ended and soundly beaten, so that the location of this boundary mark would be forever impressed upon his mind. So generations of Chetham folk remembered the significance of their great oak.

It is early spring-time. The woodland, kissed gently by the returning sun, is beginning to rub the sleep out of its eyes and to shrug off its winter lethargy. Primroses are shyly but resolutely taking their chance to absorb the sunlight before the green canopy of the tree above them excludes it. Wood anemones and wood violets share the sun with them. The deep summer shade of the oak ensures that the brambles, the thorn-bushes, the briars and the bracken are discouraged from encroaching on the perimeter, within which the lovely

and lowly flowers of spring are given adequate time to bloom.

In April, sunshine and showers proverbially alternate. The warm showers, driven ahead of south-westerly gales that peter out into breezes, impelling gardeners to frantic activity during every daylight hour, are suddenly replaced by bitter north-easters, whose accompanying grey skies and scouring snowflakes reassert, for a time, the dominance of winter. At this season, though, the final triumph of the soft Atlantic weather is inevitable, and the primroses, anemones and violets, hardier than they look, are not deceived. Nor are the early butterflies which emerge from hibernation to visit the flowers beneath the oak.

Most welcome of these visitors is the brimstone butterfly, the male so exactly the colour of a primrose that he becomes invisible when poised on one of the flowers. When suddenly he springs off and drifts away we are startled into thinking, for a moment, that the primrose itself has taken wing. This butterfly, a member of a species which has one of the longest lifespans of any British butterfly, began life as an egg in early June of last year. Throughout June and July he grew and fattened on the leaves of the buckthorn bush on the far side of the clearing. Emerging from the chrysalis about the beginning of August, he enjoyed a couple of months or so of autumn sunshine before retiring to hibernate. Reawakened by an increase in daylight and temperature in early April, he can now look forward to a further two or three months of joy, including the joy of mating, before his lifespan comes to its natural end in June.

In this life-cycle our Chetham Oak played an important role. When the time came for hibernation the butterfly chose a shelter in the dense growth of ivy which clings to the bole of the tree and billows out into a dark green cumulus around the middle branches. There it found safety for the long months of sleep.

Down in Chetham village there are conflicting opinions about that ivy. Zealous conservationists want to chop it away, lest it weaken and smother the oak. Others want to let it be. Fortunately for the brimstone butterfly, the forestry experts share the second view, as the following letter from one of them shows:

In general ivy does not do any harm to the tree on which it is growing. It is in no way parasitic and simply uses the tree as a support. By rooting in the same area of ground, the ivy must be competing to some extent for the available nutrients, but with larger trees this will not be of concern because the tree roots are deeper in the ground than the ivy and probably spreading over a far greater radius from the stem. Usually but not always ivy is only to be found growing strongly on a tree that it not too vigorous. Perhaps it is over-mature or has formed a close

5

canopy and has then been opened up but has not been able to respond by producing a large, healthy crown. Ivy may finish off an already moribund or dying tree simply by growing into the crown and suppressing the few remaining tree leaves, and this has probably caused its reputation as a killer.

Ivy may be an encumbrance to good care and maintenance of particular specimen trees by obscuring the stem and thereby disguising any rots or other damage that ought to be treated.

Other than these cases, ivy can be of benefit from the conservation point of view. It provides nesting crevices for some species of birds and sheltered night-roosting for most woodland birds, as well as shelter for butterflies and other insects, nectar for bees in late autumn, and berries for birds during winter.

Some of these creatures we shall meet again in our study of the Chetham Oak. Advocates of the hook and saw can point to the fact that the oak *is* over-mature and that the ivy may hide some of the symptoms of degeneration, but, on balance, we can be grateful that the ivy remains intact.

The brimstone butterfly joins an abundant rather than a select company. In the vast assembly of interrelated organisms that live out their brief lives within, around and beneath it, the oak supports probably a greater number of species and individuals than any other tree. It would certainly be hard to think of any tree species that could challenge the claim.

As new life starts to surge upwards through bole and branches to add one more to the oak's huge burden of summers, let us look at just one province of the Chetham Oak's domain – the soil from which it draws its sustenance.

The tree is rooted in a shallow clay cap over a deep bed of chalk, the latter formed on the floor of a shallow sea some 120 million years ago. Subsequent ages buried the chalk deep beneath deposits of reddish clay, most of which were then removed through the agency of ice. The deeper roots of the oak therefore penetrate the chalk while the shallower ones

are anchored in the clay, an arrangement doubtless of benefit
to the tree, providing a more varied range of nutrients than a
single geological stratum could.

In the spot in southern Britain appropriated by the
Chetham Oak the dominant element in both clay and chalk
subsoils is calcium. In the chalk it is mainly in the form of
calcium carbonate, a compound of great importance in deter-
mining the nature of life in the soil. The mineral base of the
soil naturally includes – besides calcium and carbon – iron,
magnesium, silicon, aluminium, sulphur and certain trace

elements, in sundry combinations with oxygen, nitrogen and hydrogen.

Agriculturists and horticulturists appreciate this sort of soil which, fortified by ample humus, can provide a splendid loam. Under cultivation the soil is continually improved by regular pulverisation and the addition of more manure, but under the oak it is not subjected to this frequent agitation. With just a few exceptions, which we shall encounter later, it has remained undisturbed for close on 1,500 years. Cracks in the clay cap allow considerable leaching of plant nutrients into the porous chalk beneath, where many of them are seized upon by the rootlets of the oak. At the same time, the annual leaf-fall replenishes the humus content of the upper layers of soil. In the absence of cultivation, the disintegration of the vegetable debris of the year is performed chiefly by soil organisms, in accordance with an exceedingly complex system evolved through the centuries.

The numbers and variety of organisms involved in these ceaseless processes are prodigious. The organisms range in size from visible and obvious creatures, such as slugs, snails, millipedes, woodlice and the larger insects, to microscopic life measured by microns (a micron is one thousandth of a milli-metre, or about one twenty-five-thousandth of an inch). Many of the soil micro-organisms are no more than 1 micron long and perhaps 0·1 to 0·2 microns in diameter.

Though they swarm in almost incredible numbers, there is plenty of room for them in the soil, which, despite its solid appearance, consists mostly of space. In grassland a century old, which can be taken to correspond approximately to the grassy clearing around the oak, the pore space accounts for about 55 per cent of the total cubic capacity of the top nine inches of soil. Rather more than half of that space is occupied by water, and lower down the proportion of water increases at the expense of pore space occupied by air. It follows that much of the microscopic life of the soil is aquatic.

Bacteria are among the most abundant of the soil denizens, and very important they are in the chain of life. It is their function to break down other organic substances, a task they accomplish in much the same way as we do. Bacteria use enzymes to transform solids into soluble substances, which they proceed to digest. There is hardly a known substance, including many man-made synthetic ones of recent origin, which some bacterium or another cannot recycle in this way. Of the waste products of the process, surplus to what the bacteria can absorb, much carbon is converted to carbon dioxide and dissipates into the air, while surplus nitrogen becomes ammonia and is stored in the soil as a reserve of plant food. Eventually, when the bacteria die the mineral constituents of their bodies are also added to that reserve or are used by other organisms.

Fungi of many types are another important group of soil inhabitants. They include numerous moulds and mildews besides the mycelia of the larger fungi, such as mushrooms. Their function is similar to that of bacteria. They feed on decaying organic matter, absorbing and recycling the proteins and carbohydrates in plant and animal residues. On death they are taken over by bacteria, which release their accumulation of nitrogen and other elements for use by other creatures.

Associated with soil fungi but even smaller than most of them are the actinomycetes. Their spores resemble those of bacteria in appearance, but in due course they produce threads of mycelium after the manner of fungi. Many of them manufacture antibiotics. Scientists are still divided as to whether the actinomycetes are really bacteria or fungi or an intermediate form of life. What is indisputable is that they are exceedingly numerous. One experiment has revealed from 10 to 15 million of their spores in a single gram of soil.

Algae are minute but rather more sophisticated organisms. Although consisting of single cells or filaments, they have the power of extracting carbon dioxide from the air, combining it with water and transforming it, through the use of sunlight, into sugars. In other words, they have mastered the process of photosynthesis, an achievement which gives many of them a green colour. Some species, however, which have the ability to take nitrogen from the air, are coloured blue-green or blue. The numbers of algae in the soil are extremely high, though less so than some other micro-organisms. Up to 3 million have

9

been recorded per gram of some soils.

Protozoa are the predators of the micro-world of the soil. They feed primarily on bacteria and other tiny organisms. The names of two major groups, namely the amoebae and the flagellates, will be familiar to all who have peered through a microscope at school. Estimates of population, made at Rothamsted and other experimental stations, indicate a level about one-tenth of that of bacteria and fungal mycelia – a healthy predator/prey ratio.

Bacteriophages are mysterious organisms, visible only with the aid of an electron microscope. They prey on bacteria (and some on actinomycetes) by forcing themselves inside the bacteria cells and dissolving the entire contents. Most species of bacteria have their own specific bacteriophages. In size bacteriophages range from about 0·1 to 0·01 microns.

Other soil micro-organisms include the myxococci, which absorb bacteria by first liquefying their bodies. They are very numerous in some soils. There are also giant rhizopods, which range up to 3 mm in diameter and which feed on amoebae. So too do an anomalous group of micro-organisms, the Acrasieae, which apparently behave sometimes like amoebae and sometimes like fungi.

Compared with these microscopic creatures the visible fauna of the soil are monsters, though to our eyes they appear extremely small. At the lower end of the scale, just visible to us, are certain arthropods, nematodes and insects.

Most numerous of the arthropods (which include the spiders) are the Acarinae or mites. One survey of the arthropod population of grassland has revealed about 1,400 million per acre, of which about 950 million were mites. Other investigations have recorded populations of double and even treble those levels. Acarinae present in the soil live mostly on decaying vegetable matter, but some on decaying animal matter, including animal droppings. They thus perform a useful service in recycling the debris that arrives in the soil.

Nematodes, or eelworms, are thread-like creatures of considerable versatility. Some are parasitic on plants, some on animals, and some are independent of both. Most range from 0·5 mm to 1·5 mm in length, but there exist in the tropical world nematodes several feet long. Soil nematodes seem to feed primarily if not entirely on other soil organisms, especially bacteria. They are most plentiful in grassland, where they concentrate in the top two inches of soil. A Danish investigation has shown a population of from 4 to 20 million nematodes per square metre of grassland.

Of the micro-insects of the soil by far the most numerous are the Collembola or springtails. They are strange creatures for whom evolution seems to have stopped in the Lower Devonian era, some 300 million years ago. In size they range from 0·3 mm to 5 mm, which means that the larger ones are easily visible to us. In spring the detritus beneath the oak seems alive with agile life, whose movements we can detect though the insects themselves have gone before we can spot them. These springtails have elongated, segmented bodies, prominent antennae and, at their rear end, a peculiar catapult-like organ which enables them to make prodigious leaps. If a man could match their performance he would need to be able to register 750 to 900 feet in the long jump. Collembola feed on both plant and animal residues and so are useful recycling agents. A survey of the insect population of grassland has recorded a total of 379 million per acre, of which 248 million, or about two-thirds, were Collembola. Most of them were in the top six inches of soil.

It is rather intriguing though perhaps not particularly profitable to attempt some rough estimates of the numbers of these micro-organisms and macro-organisms which form a part – the subterranean part – of the commonwealth of the oak.

The Chetham Oak, with its canopy diameter of 240 feet, claims a surface territory of 45,216 square feet, which is a little over an acre. So the figures per acre quoted above for the insect population can stand for the population in the domain of the oak. Similarly we can accept an arthropod population of about 1,400 million, of which about 950 million are mites. When we come to the bacteria, the algae and other minute fry, however, the figures are so colossal as to be virtually meaningless. Counts of the bacteria in a gram of soil range from about 20 million to 1,000 million or even 4,000 million. A gram of soil is the equivalent of 0·002205 of a pound. An acre of soil to the depth of nine inches weighs approximately 1000 tons, or 2,240,000 pounds. There we have the basic figures for our calculations. Taking the medium level of 1,000 million bacteria per gram of soil, a kilogram will contain 1,000,000 million bacteria. Therefore one pound of soil contains 1,000,000 millions divided by 2·205, which gives 453,514·7 millions. And 1,000 tons of soil contains 453,514·7 millions multiplied by 2,240,000 bacteria, a figure so astronomical that we would hardly have room for it on this page. And that is the bacterial population of the ground immediately surrounding the Chetham Oak.

Similar approximate populations for some of the other micro-organisms can be worked out, by those with a mathematical bent, from the following data:

10 to 15 millions of fungi spores per gram of soil
(a Rothamsted Experimental Station figure for grassland).
200,000 to 3 million algae per gram of soil.
1,000 rhizopods per gram of soil.
2,000 to 76,000 myxococci per gram of soil.

To get these bewildering figures into some sort of perspective it may be useful to recall that an American lady once typed out all the numbers from one to one million. It took her 5½ years and required 2500 sheets of paper. Just *one* million.

Also that two saltspoons of soil would contain more bacteria (at the rate of 4,000 millions per gram) than the total human population of the earth.

Of the larger fauna of the soil beneath the Chetham Oak, earthworms can claim an impressive population figure. From 2 to 3 million per acre is an accepted total for old grassland, so we can assume that that is an approximate figure for the total sheltered by our oak.

This teeming population is kept perennially busy dealing with the leaf-fall from the great tree. Just over a hundred years ago Charles Darwin asserted that all the surface soil of Britain had 'passed many times through, and will again pass many times through, the intestinal canal of worms'. Collecting worm-casts daily and weighing them, Darwin arrived at an average total of ten tons per acre per year processed by earthworms, and that takes no account of certain earthworms which do not make casts. The earthworms under the Chetham Oak are thus shifting ten tons or so of soil and vegetable matter every year. They are, of course, extracting from the soil the decaying vegetable matter on which they largely feed (though they readily take animal matter as well).

Other soil inhabitants, some of which will feature in later chapters, include centipedes, millipedes, woodlice, the larvae of numerous insects, slugs, snails and ants. Some of them live on vegetable matter, and are considered as pests when they occur in the garden. Some are carnivorous. In general they are important as the food of large and more advanced types of animal life, such as birds.

Into this subterranean world with its complex, bewildering patterns of life the roots of the great oak probe, seeking nourishment. Massive, trunk-like roots divide into lesser branches, which further split and subdivide as they penetrate deep into the soil. From the tiniest root tips hair-like fibres search among the soil particles for the nutrients the plant needs. These they capture by the process of osmosis, by which water flows naturally from a substance with a low salt concentration, like the soil, to one with a high salt concentration – the plant hairs. It follows, of course, that moisture, meaning a damp soil, is necessary, for the root hairs can absorb minerals only in solution.

The minerals collected by the roots from the depths of the soil must then be transported to the leaves which are to utilise them. This is done by an arrangement of tube-like cells called xylem vessels, which extend from the root system to the twigs and leaves. Their importance is underlined by the position they occupy in the tree's anatomy, deep in the heartwood and protected by layers of cambium and bark. Once received by the xylem vessels, the minerals, in a highly concentrated solution, set out on their tremendous journey, uphill all the way, to the distant leaf-buds.

The mechanics of the operation are still a bit of a mystery. How does the tree manage to raise a continuous flow of minerals in solution from roots to leaves? On a sunny summer day our oak may have to convey more than 100 gallons of nutrient-laden water for a vertical distance of perhaps 100 feet.

The explanation probably lies in the action of the leaves. On the underside of an oak leaf are several millions of pores or stomata, through which the leaf breathes in air and exhales oxygen. Naturally through the same pores it also loses water by transpiration. On a hot summer day the loss may amount to more than 90 per cent of the water entering the leaf. This results in the water being sucked up through the roots, trunks, branches and twigs by a process analagous to that of a vacuum pump.

Like all green plants, the oak lives and grows by that marvellous manufacturing process, photosynthesis. The factories are the leaves, and the power they use is sunlight. The essential process consists of extraction by the leaves of carbon from the air and its combination with minerals to form sugars and ultimately other carbohydrates and proteins. Sunlight, shining through the chlorophyll, the green pigment of the leaves, supplies the energy.

From the leaves the complex compounds they have manufactured flow to every part of the tree through another system of pipe-like cells known as the phloem vessels, supplying it with energy and the means of growth. Very similar in construction to the xylem vessels, the phloem cells are located nearer the surface of the trunk and branches, the uppermost layers being just beneath the bark. They are what we strike when we cut through bark and see the sap flowing.

The reason for the towering stature and mighty expanse of the oak thus becomes obvious. Its leaves are, in effect, solar panels, which the tree spreads in a broad and high canopy in order to trap as much sunlight as possible. Every leaf of the oak is so arranged that it catches rays of sunlight at some time on a clear day, even if only for a few minutes.

Every year, until it reaches maturity (which, of course, was long ago with the Chetham Oak), the tree thrusts out new twigs to increase its height and expanse and thus the total surface areas of its leaves. Every year, too, it adds a new layer of cells of woody tissue just beneath the bark, thus, year by year, increasing the diameter of its trunk. In the course of this programme, a time comes when the cells of the inner layers are no longer required for conveying water and minerals from roots to leaves. So they die, but, being sealed in behind living tissue, they remain part of the tree, which utilises them even in death. They become embalmed and mummified, their tubes now filled with preservatives such a tannin, to form immensely strong heartwood. Thus fortified, the oak sturdily supports the great weight of its spreading crown and withstands the battering of winter gales.

The cycle of the seasons, in the temperate zones which are the natural home of the oak, is clearly recorded in the growth of the tree. As in Britain the short northern summer slides to its close and the oak prepares for its winter sleep, a corky plug forms at the junction of the leaf and its twig, cutting off the supply of mineral food from the roots. The sap recedes. The leaves, their role fulfilled, clothe the oak in glorious golden splendour as they slowly die. Falling to the ground, they disintegrate and are absorbed into the soil, as the food of the multitudinous micro-organisms which are waiting for them. Eventually they are broken down into their constituent minerals which next year will be available for the tree's roots. If we could eat and draw nourishment from our discarded hair and finger-nails, that would be an analogy of the oak's efficient system for recycling nutrients.

The amount of wood added by a summer's growth naturally varies according to the summer weather. In a wet year the tree produces a wide zone of new tissue to enlarge its trunk; in a dry year, a narrow one. The woody growth it makes early in the season is light in colour; the later additions, a dark brown. A cross-section of a tree-trunk therefore provides by its concentric rings an annual record of the weather throughout the entire life of the tree. And a series of tree-trunks of overlapping ages can provide a chronological weather table extending over the centuries. Once established, it provides a yardstick by which timbers from archaeological sites can be dated, thus forming the basis of the recently developed science of dendrochronology.

The sudden movement of the brimstone butterfly as he takes wing attracts the notice of a chiffchaff, who has been energetically searching for insect eggs on the outer twigs of one of the lower branches of the oak. The butterfly easily evades the bird's foray and sails away on majestic wingbeats. The chiffchaff returns to his twig and resumes his search.

Like the butterfly, the chiffchaff is a male. He arrived from Africa only a few days ago, at the end of March. As with most migrating birds, he is here two or three weeks in advance of the females, his role being to establish a suitable breeding territory. However, here at the Chetham Oak he is just practising his penetrating, aggressive song – 'chiff-chaff-chiffchaff' – for he will not stay long. He is on his way to ancestral nesting grounds farther north, but, like his ancestors for untold generations, is using the oak as a convenient stopping-place en route. The oak, the way to it, and the invisible route from it to his destination are details built into his genetic heredity. He cannot change them, any more than he can change the pattern of his song or the method of nest-building. Here he must rest for a few days, to recuperate and replenish his fuel supplies after the prodigious journey from Africa.

His winter quarters are in savannah country along the southern fringe of the Sahara, where he has been sharing the thorn-bushes and water-holes by the Gambia with such exotic species as the blue-bellied roller, the paradise flycatcher and the carmine bee-eater. Why he should ever bother to make the journey from that climate to the chilly storm-lands of the north (an almost incredible journey for a bird measuring only just over four inches and weighing about half an ounce) is a mystery that has puzzled generations of naturalists. The very long days, which give parent birds the maximum amount of time for collecting food for growing nestlings, would seem to be the chief advantage gained. No completely satisfactory theory to account for the development of migration has yet been postulated, however.

16

One indisputable fact is that the annual journeys are becoming longer and more hazardous. Eight thousand years ago the Sahara was a vast region of undulating grasslands and wooded hills, reasonably well watered and inhabited by myriads of grazing animals, as well as by tribes of humans. For some unexplained reason the prairies began to dry up and become a desert, and the process is still continuing. Every year the margin of vegetation retreats a few more miles southwards, so increasing the distances the migrant birds have to travel over inhospitable wastes.

In preparation for his exacting journey our chiffchaff fattened up in his African home before setting out. Stimulated by chemical changes in his body, he acquired a more insatiable appetite than normal and was consequently much more active in search of food. In the course of a few weeks his weight increased from about 0·4 oz to 0·8 oz. The chiffchaff thus took aboard enough fuel to last for 60 to 90 hours of non-stop flight. Travelling at about 30 m.p.h., with wings beating twelve to fifteen times a second, he was able to cross the wide Sahara in 30 or 40 hours, which gave a wide margin of safety. He was lucky enough to escape the violent sandstorms which often cause heavy casualties among migrating birds.

Like most small song-birds, he travelled chiefly by night. Once he was across the desert, this gave him a chance to spend the daylight hours catching insects to replenish his fuel supplies. By the time he reached the Chetham Oak his weight was already back to normal, namely the 0·4 oz he weighed before he started stoking up for his voyage.

His preoccupation with food on this fine spring morning must be blamed for his inattention to other matters, a lapse which almost cost him his life. A sparrow-hawk, which works by stealth and speed, had spotted him and marked him out for its next victim. It glided in swiftly and silently, keeping as much cover as possible between it and the chiffchaff. At the last moment it swerved into the open and made a dash for its prey. The doom of the chiffchaff would have been inevitable, but for the intervention of the hawk's arch-enemy, man.

The man was no more aware of the sparrow-hawk than was

the chiffchaff, but the hawk saw him. Veering frantically, it shot off amid the branches, endeavouring to place the tree as a barrier between it and this most dreaded of all menaces. The chiffchaff, alerted at last and impelled by a surge of adrenalin, dived instinctively into the ivy. The man alone in this minor drama remained impassive and unconcerned. He had caught a brief glimpse of the retreating hawk but was unaware of the presence of the chiffchaff. His thoughts were of the tracks he had been studying along a forest ride, tracks of two largish dogs. Poaching dogs, loose without an owner, he surmised. For some of their foot-prints had half obliterated the slots of the roe deer, and uncontrolled dogs hunting the does now heavy with young were the last thing he wanted in his wood.

Noyce is his name, Jim Noyce. He is the forest warden. He started his woodland career as under-keeper to his father, John Noyce, when the forest was part of the Earl of Melhurst's estate. The Noyces had been keepers on the estate ever since it had been enormously extended by enclosure in the eighteenth century. Their ancestor at that time had been one of the more adaptable peasants who, confronted with the obliteration of their common rights and of their former way of life, chose to come to terms with their new master rather than decamp to the new industrial slums of iron and coal, as so many did.

They were tenacious, the Noyces. They never doubted that this was where they belonged, and here they intended to stay. They knew that their family had always lived at Chetham, though they could not put a term of years to the word 'always'. It led, in fact, farther into the past than they could have imagined. A Noyce had guided King Charles through the forest when he was a fugitive after the Battle of Worcester. A Noyce had helped build on Chetham Hill the bonfire that was a link in the chain carrying across England the news of the sighting of the Armada. Noyce, a bowman, had brought his family a modest and temporary prosperity in the shape of French loot, lugged home after the battle of Agincourt. A Saxon Noyce had watched with glum apprehension the arrival of the Norman knight (Greville de Courcy)

18

and his men-at-arms when they came to take possession of the manor at the time of the Conquest.

A Noyce had watched the departure of the last cohorts of the Roman legions in the twilight hours of the old civilisation, though then he was called Gnaeus. Phonetically, the name is recognisable as 'Noyce'. Just as, among his Chetham neighbours, Fred Gay has a name which was originally Gaius, Bill Yeates had an ancestor whose name was Aëtius, and Martin Titt's family name is really the good Latin name of Titus.

Such information is outside the ambit of Jim Noyce. He was a keeper, trained to kill creatures classified as vermin; now he is warden of a nature reserve, protecting the wildlife which he once sought out with a double-barrelled shotgun. But it is *his* forest, and he takes orders from whoever is in a position to issue them. Efficient, conscientious, honest, the Noyces and the oak are indeed features of the forest. Jim, in fact, is more a part of the Forest than he realises, for, did he but know it, he was conceived under the oak one May night some forty-five years ago. Though possibly, if he ever thought about it, he may have guessed, for time-old associations with the oak, crystallised into custom, still linger in Chetham.

2

THE OAK IN SPRING

THE WORLD of the forest is in a ferment. The factories of the soil are in full production and working overtime. The bacteria, the micro-fungi, the actinomycetes, the bacteriophages, the protozoans, the algae, the acarina, the nematodes, the springtails and the other teeming subterranean hordes, stimulated by the rising temperature and the abundance of moisture, are frantically processing scraps of organic matter in their digestive tracts and releasing its constituent elements into the soil, where they are now in demand in vast quantities.

For it is May-time, the season when prodigious growth is imperative. Though the last frosts are still a recent memory, midsummer lies only six weeks ahead. So short is the northern summer, so brief the period into which all life has to cram its reproductive activities.

The lowly plants of field and forest, having tentatively sent up leaves and stems to test the environment while the threat of winter still lingered, are now pouring all their resources into the all-important task of ensuring the survival of their species. That involves producing seed, for which a necessary preliminary is fertilisation. So cow parsley, stitchwort, blue-bell, wild strawberry, cuckoo-flower, cinquefoil, columbine, bugle, wild geranium, avens, lily-of-the-valley, yellow arch-angel and all the other woodland plants are making haste to attract by colour, form and scent the insects on which they depend. Having extracted from the living soil the ingredients they need, they employ them in fashioning artistic master-pieces beyond human power to emulate. Consider the archi-tecture of a cowslip. What human architect would ever attempt to balance such a top-heavy superstructure on such a slender stem?

The task undertaken by the oak is even more exacting. By its exploring rootlets it has to extract the minerals it needs from greater depths than its herbaceous neighbours can ever penetrate and then convey them, via the highways of roots, trunks, branches and twigs to the buds from which it, too, like all flowering plants, must produce its seed. As noted in Chapter 1, it may be required to raise 100 gallons of nutrient-laden water to the tips of its twigs every day, and the traffic goes on without ceasing throughout the months of spring and early summer.

Its leaves, as we have seen, play an essential part in the process, and the oak must unfurl its full canopy as soon as the weather allows.

The flowering of the oak, which follows almost immedi-ately, is not a spectacular event. Because they are pollinated by the wind instead of by insects the flowers do not need to flaunt vivid colours or striking patterns or to produce a heady fragrance as do lowlier plants. The female flowers are extremely inconspicuous. They have no petals. Each consists of a three-chambered ovary surmounted by three styles (little

21

stalks bearing the stigmas to which the pollen adheres). It is true that the styles are coloured crimson, but they add little to the visual attractions of the oak, for they are almost too small to be appreciated by the naked eye. The male flowers are slightly larger and are arranged loosely on catkin stems. Each flower has, as a rule, from five to seven pollen-producing stamens (though occasionally more) and an equal number of green sepals, but no petals. The flowering of the oak is therefore an event of such low key that it can be missed by anyone who does not especially look for it.

A well-known rural proverb states:

When the ash comes out before the oak,
The summer will bring a regular soak;
When the oak comes out before the ash,
Then we shall only get a splash.

But, apart from arguing about whether the term 'coming out' refers to the flowers or the leaves, it is doubtful whether anyone, at least in recent years, has tested the truth of it. My impression is that the ash usually flowers before the oak, which tallies very well with the fact that English summers are generally wet.

Although we may fail to observe just when the oak flowers, certain insects which depend on the tree for their existence may naturally be relied upon to be on hand at the critical moment. Enter the gall-flies, or, to give them their alternative name, the gall-wasps. They are technically not flies, being members of the order Hymenoptera, to which bees, wasps and ants also belong. They are tiny, black, four-winged insects so insignificant that they might easily be dismissed as of no importance. The mighty oak, however, has every reason to be aware of their activities.

The gall-fly that takes its name from the oak, though it is not the most abundant species infesting the tree, is the oak-apple gall-fly (*Biorrhiza terminalis*). Its galls are rather large, soft, spongy growths, 5 to 10 cm in diameter, growing from the twigs. When fresh they are creamy-white in colour but they soon become streaked and diffused with green and pink. These are the true oak-apples, though sometimes other galls are given that name.

Gall-flies in general have quite remarkable life histories, and the oak-apple gall-fly is no exception. The oak-apple is the home not of a single grub but of a colony of larvae, each with its own tiny cell. By about midsummer they have finished growing, have completed a brief pupal stage and are ready to emerge into adult life. If when we examine an oak-apple at this season we find it studded with pin-holes, we shall know that the gall-flies have matured and escaped. This brood of adult insects, both male and female, are all winged. They fly around in the summer sunshine and mate.

Thereafter the behaviour of the female gall-fly departs from the normal insect pattern. Instead of returning to the oak-twig which bore her natal oak-apple she makes her way to the base of the tree-trunk and disappears underground. In the deep, dark soil cavities around the roots she seeks out suitable rootlets and on them lays her eggs. When the larvae emerge they too are responsible for galls, but hard, woody, blackish galls, not a bit like oak-apples. Inside these galls the larvae feed and eventually pupate.

Somewhere around the winter solstice the adult gall-flies emerge from these pupae. But these are very different in appearance from the gall-flies which ate their way out of the oak-apple. For one thing they are all females; for another, they are without wings. Tiny, yellowish-brown insects, they undertake in midwinter the long, arduous climb up the trunk and along the branches to the outermost twigs of the oak. There, unmated, they lay their tiny, pear-shaped eggs in the tight terminal buds from which the oak leaves and flowers should develop. The eggs, a mass of them, are meticulously inserted between the protecting scales of the growing tip of the bud. When in spring the bud starts to grow the oak tries to isolate it from this irritating intrusion by surrounding the larvae with the abnormal tissue which develops into the gall. That, at least, is the theory usually advanced to explain the gall's formation, though another is that the larvae themselves

23

excrete a substance which causes the protective tissue to form, while yet another holds that the gall-fly injects the bud with such a substance at the time of egg-laying. Whatever the chemistry involved, the life-cycle of the gall-fly is completed when the oak-apple is vacated by the generation which hatches the following midsummer – a generation of flies which exactly resemble their grandparents but are quite unlike their virgin mother.

Another gall frequently called an oak-apple is the marble gall, produced by a gall-fly called *Cynips* or *Andricus kollari*. The gall is most conspicuous in autumn, when it has served its purpose and has hardened into a brown, woody ball, about the same size as a marble or a cherry.

The clean-cut round hole through which the insect escaped is clearly visible. Each marble gall contains only one larva, a plump, juicy, white grub much appreciated by tits and woodpeckers, who often demolish the walls of the gall to get at it. Although the life-cycle of the marble gall-fly has not yet been properly worked out it is thought to be similar to that of the oak-apple gall-fly, having alternate and unlike generations.

The leaves of the oak are host to several species of gall. One of the commonest is the silk-button gall (*Neuroterus numismatis*), with which the underside of oak leaves are frequently studded. Sometimes there are scores of them on a single leaf. The galls are tiny flat discs with a central depression, and they are fixed to the leaf by only a flimsy stalk, which makes it easy for them to be detached in autumn. Dropping to the ground, they are quickly buried by falling leaves, under which they spend the winter. In spring the perfect insects emerge and lay their eggs in the oak's leaf-buds, but the resultant galls are quite different from the silk-button galls. They even have their own name – blister galls – which is accurately descriptive. From these pale green galls a new generation of perfect insects emerges in June, and these are the gall-flies whose

larvae are responsible for the
formation of the silk-button galls.

A somewhat similar complicated
life history belongs to another
common oak-leaf gall, the spangle
gall. These galls resemble silk-
button galls but are rather larger
and have raised instead of concave
centres. They are purplish-brown in
colour. Like the silk-button galls, they
become detached in autumn and fall to
the ground, to be buried under decaying leaves.
Then in spring the emerging gall-flies, all females, make their
way to the tips of the oak-twigs and there lay their eggs. But
the resultant gall in no way resembles the spangle gall.
Instead, it is a round red gall which appears on the stems
bearing the tree's male catkins. Sometimes
they occupy an entire stem and, because
they look like a string of red currants,
are known as currant galls.
As with marble galls,
there is only one larva in
each gall. It speeds through
its development at such a
pace that the perfect insects
(both male and female) emerge
in June. The females of this
generation lay their eggs, not
singly but in clusters, on the oak's
leaves, where in due course they
produce spangle galls. The scientific
name of the gall-fly with this strange series of metamorphoses
is *Neuroterus quercusbaccarum*.

Two other gall-flies parasitic on the oak which go in for
alternate generations are the hop gall or artichoke gall (*Andricus fecundatrix*) and the cherry gall (*Dryophanta scutellaris*). The
hop gall, a fairly common species, derives its name from its
resemblance to a hop-cone or artichoke head, the oak bud
leaves having produced a cluster of distorted leaf-scales in an

25

attempt to protect themselves against the intrusive larvae. The entire gall falls off in autumn and is buried under discarded leaves. When the females emerge in spring they lay their eggs on the oak-buds due to produce male catkins, so the resultant galls appear on the catkin stems. They are oval, green excrescences, so tiny as to be hardly noticeable, and are known as hairy catkin galls.

Cherry galls are conspicuous round galls, sometimes as much as 3 centimetres in diameter, attached to the underside of oak leaves. At first they are green, changing to yellow and eventually to rosy pink. They appear later in summer than the other galls, and the perfect insects do not emerge until the autumn is well advanced. The females then lay their eggs on the dormant buds which will produce leaves the following year. The galls resulting from this generation of eggs are not cherry galls but are known as violet egg galls, because they are egg-shaped and, when mature, are coloured violet. They are, however, so small and insignificant that they need to be specially searched for. It is the females which emerge from these galls around the end of May which are responsible for the cherry galls later in the summer.

None of these galls presents a serious problem to the mature oak, which has learned to live with them for a long time, though if too numerous they can sap the strength of saplings. At one time alarm bells rang for the marble galls, which are not indigenous to Britain but which were introduced about the year 1834. Tradition has it that the introduction was made because the galls were used in dye-manufacturing. Anne Pratt, a distinguished botanist writing around the turn of the century, puts the story the other way round, implying that scientists started looking for commercial possibilities in the galls *after* they had become well established. Fears that the galls would seriously damage the oak woods of England seem to have been rife during the nineteenth century but have proved to be unfounded.

However, a new gall, first reported in England in the early 1970s, has been heralded as a much more serious potential menace. Known as the knopper gall, it results from the activities of the gall-fly *Andricus quercuscalicis*, which, like so many gall-flies, has a highly complex life-cycle. The part of the oak attacked in summer is the acorn. The galls more or less take over the acorn cup and apparently achieve a 90 per cent kill. Existing oaks are not particularly inconvenienced, but of course their ability to reproduce themselves is impaired, and foresters are worried.

One limiting factor is that one phase in the life of *Andricus quercuscalicis* has to be spent on the Turkey oak, a rather uncommon species in England. The tiny insects, however, have quite astonishing powers of flight and from one Turkey oak can disperse over an area with a radius of tens of miles. Another hopeful factor is that grey squirrels seem to be as fond of knopper galls as they are of acorns.

As members, albeit parasitic ones, of the commonwealth of the oak, gall-flies are a well defined group of the 500 or so insect species which find their living in or under the oak's vast canopy. Most of the others are parasites or predators, too.

No sooner has the oak unfolded its leaves than hordes of insect larvae arrive to attack them. One of the most formidable aggressors is the green tortrix moth (*Tortrix viridana*) whose larvae appear in such numbers in

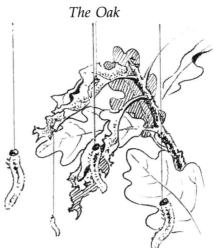

some years that they almost defoliate the tree. The moth, pale-green in colour, is quite a small one, and its insignificant caterpillars achieve their devastating effects by sheer numbers. When feeding they conceal themselves in rolled-up leaves fastened by silk, and if disturbed they quickly lower themselves to the ground by silken strands.

The green tortrix belongs to the class of moths known as micro-moths, most of which are too small to attract the interest of collectors and which therefore have no popular English names. With similar life-styles to that of the green tortrix, they are of considerable importance to the oak. *Phycita, Acrobasis, Cryptoblabes* and *Endrotricha* are the names of some of the moths whose larvae are sufficiently numerous to make an impact on the oak's canopy. Some of these little caterpillars associate in colonies, protected by closely-spun webs; some are solitary, hiding themselves in a folded leaf.

Of the larger or macro-moths, the caterpillars of well over a hundred species derive their livelihood from the oak. From mid-May to mid-June beating the foliage of an oak so that the dislodged insects fall on a cloth spread underneath or a tray or an upturned umbrella can reveal surprising results. The commonest larvae are those of the geometrid moths – the well-known looper caterpillars, many of which, like the micros, conceal themselves in little leaf-tents fastened with silk. Some of the larger ones adopt other forms of camouflage, the caterpillar of the great oak beauty, for instance, being adept at remaining motionless in a stilted position and pretending it is an oak twig. Several moths, including the oak beauty, the pale oak beauty, the great oak beauty, the oak hook-tip and the oak-tree pug, take their names from their mighty host.

The caterpillars of one group of moths, the footman moths, feed on the lichens growing on the trunk and branches of the oak, as do the extremely well camouflaged caterpillars of the dotted carpet moth, while those of the common fanfoot moth feed themselves on the dead leaves of the oak on the woodland floor.

Curiously the caterpillars of only one British butterfly, the purple hairstreak, feed on the foliage of the oak, though those of the holly blue may sometimes be found on the ivy embracing an old tree such as our Chetham Oak.

Naturally, this profusion of insect life attracts predators, the most prominent of which are birds.

The chiffchaff which sang temporarily in the oak in early April is now shouting his claim to a nesting territory in Derbyshire, but another has taken his place. The hen is sitting on her six glossy red-speckled white eggs in a nest built low in a tangle of bramble and honeysuckle at the edge of the clearing, while the indolent male selects a convenient perch on the oak itself. Indolent he undoubtedly is, for he left his mate to build the nest unaided, and very soon she alone will be undertaking the duties of feeding the young.

Both chiffchaffs take their toll of the insect hordes, as do the pair of wrens nesting in the ivy on the oak's bole and the hedge sparrows which occupy a nesting site on the far side of the clearing. A week ago a nightingale dropped in and

29

proceeded to advertise his presence with full-throated contralto melodies by day and by night. It is a fallacy to suppose that nightingales are exclusively nocturnal. Their song period is short, extending for only six or eight weeks from their date of arrival to mid-June, but during it the cock nightingale will exercise his voice at any hour of the day or night. Toss a stone into a bush near his perch (though that is not really recommended) and he will react with vigorous song.

As an insect eater the nightingale takes his part in dealing with the insect invasion of the oak, assisted by the blackbirds, tits, woodpeckers, nuthatches, tree-creepers, goldfinches, chaffinches, bullfinches and other small birds that live in Chetham Wood. The oak's most effective allies are, however, rather surprisingly, rooks and jays. Jays are always present in the forest, though they prefer fruit, nuts and vegetables to small insects, but the rooks, which live in a rookery in Chetham village, normally forage in the open fields and seldom venture into the woods. The superabundant larvae, however, are an irresistible temptation, and from morning to night they come gliding in to alight on the oak and squabble vociferously over the feast.

Nor does dusk bring an end to the feeding activities on and around the oak. While the voracious caterpillars continue to feed, so do the predators for whom they represent a meal. The resident robin of this part of the wood works late, sharing the twilight with the bats who swoop in to capture the moths that are the parents of the larvae. A wandering hedgehog, making far more noise among the dead leaves than his size warrants, feasts on the larvae that have fallen from the tree. He is joined by a male woodcock whose mate is sitting close on a clutch of brown-blotched eggs, near hatching point, against the trunk of one of the younger oaks of the forest. The green sward of the clearing, close-grazed by deer, is a favourite foraging-ground for the woodcock, who likes to dig there for earth-worms, but the fallen caterpillars now littering the ground provide an easier and equally appetising meal.

Presently satiated, the woodcock rises and indulges in his peculiar display flight, known to naturalists as 'roding'. On attaining a height of about thirty feet he circles the clearing on slow-flapping wings, much like a butterfly, and then sets off along one of the rides towards the heart of the forest, uttering as he goes a thin but penetrating double note – 'tsiwick'. Sometimes he meets another male in the ride and they engage in a ritual display. Presumably the incubating female is keeping an eye on the whole performance.

Another spectator is the roe deer doe, suckling her twin fawns, born only five days ago, in bushes not far from the chiffchaff's nest. The plethora of caterpillars is of no interest to her, but, by helping to keep the grass close-nibbled and so provide a table on which food-seekers can readily find their prey, she too plays her part in the Commonwealth of the Oak.

Jim Noyce is by no means the only forest dweller owing his origin to a romantic encounter under the great oak. A few of the villagers who come here, year by year, on Oak-Apple Day (29 May) to uphold what they have been told has been a custom from time immemorial have a suspicion that there was more to the ancient traditions than meets the eye. They can only conjecture, so they loyally go through the honoured ritual, as bequeathed by their grandparents.

Very early in the morning, when the sky is still grey even at this date so near midsummer, they trudge by long-remembered paths into the heart of Chetham Forest. There they cut from the young oaks green boughs to be dragged down to Chetham village, there to decorate the exteriors of the houses and the church. Prizes are offered for the most effective display and also for the branches bearing the most oak-apples. After numerous past arguments involving non-botanist organisers, all kinds of gall are now accepted as oak-apples.

In times past the bough-gathering was centred on the Chetham Oak, but to lop its venerable branches now would be regarded with the same disapproval as chipping flakes of stone off Stonehenge. So the younger trees are subjected to a pruning, though utility-minded gardeners ignore the oaks

entirely and use the occasion to accumulate a supply of ash and hazel rods, for supporting beans and peas.

Later in the day a religious service is held in Chetham parish church, a fête is staged on the village green, and in the evening lads and lasses dance on the grass to the music of the village band. So Chetham Oak Apple Day is celebrated for yet another year. Today's generation of Chetham villagers believe that by so doing they are perpetuating their rights to use certain footpaths through the forest, and perhaps that is an element in the ancient ritual. That, however, was not the interpretation put on the festival when the old oak was young.

The date of the celebration has wandered about the calendar during the course of centuries. Most of the customs originated, far back, with May Day, but before the calendar was changed in 1752 May Day itself was eleven days later in the year. Most of the age-old customs lapsed during the period of the Commonwealth in the seventeenth century, the Puritans having no love for what they regarded as frivolous and pernicious superstitions. Then, when the interregnum was over and 'Old England was merry again', many of the May Day celebrations were transferred, on revival, to 29 May, henceforth known as Oak-Apple Day, to commemorate King Charles II's escape after the Battle of Worcester by hiding in the Boscobel Oak.

That is a summary of their recent history, but, much farther back, they have their origin in prehistoric and pagan times. Primarily fertility rites, they are associated with the fertilising spirit of vegetation, who, after his long winter sleep, was obviously very much alive and active at this season. The green boughs brought from the forest to decorate the village houses were symbols of the ancient god of fertility. The Green Man, later Jack-o'-the-Green or the Chimney Sweep, was a representation of him. The maypole was his phallus. The original morris dancers, careering around it in tight circles, were performing powerful magic. So were the youths and girls who spent the night of May Day Eve in the greenwood – and if the result was a new crop of babies nine months hence, that was the purpose of the exercise. In days when a man's first illness was almost certainly his last, the tribe needed constant replenishment to keep up its numeric strength, and that, after all, was what young people were for.

The old oak has seen it all. England was not even nominally Christian when the Chetham Oak was young, and for centuries afterwards the Christian ethic was confined largely to the ruling classes. The forest dwellers adhered to their ancient lore until only just beyond the horizon of living memory. Did his parents, in the pride of their lusty youth, know they were acting according to immemorial custom that May night when Jim was conceived under the old oak? It seems likely enough.

The spring equinox is the time for awakening from the winter sleep. Already the first primroses and daffodils are in bloom, and tiny leaves, no bigger than a mouse's ear, are venturing out of their tight buds. The countryside is beginning to vibrate and pulsate with life, and not least the oak which with a powerful rhythm is pumping nutrient-laden sap from the recesses of the soil to the outermost buds and twigs of its canopy.

Men in many ages and of many cultures have known this and benefited from it. Bismarck, Germany's Iron Chancellor, when his vitality was at a low ebb would stand for half an hour with his back against the trunk of a great oak, absorbing its strength. North American Indians, too, came to the oak for renewal in the same manner. Some sensitive persons have testified to hearing the oak 'singing', much as telephone poles 'sing' when clasped.

So when Jim Noyce leans against the trunk of his Chetham Oak he is not, as may appear, idling away his time. Presently he will stride away, feeling renewed and invigorated.

3

THE OAK IN HIGH SUMMER

THE TORTRIX caterpillars have departed, as suddenly as a crowd dispersed by a thunderstorm. One day the oak seemed alive with them; the next they had vanished. A column of safari ants could not have eliminated them more thoroughly. Plenty of other caterpillars remain, however, their life-cycles not coinciding with that of the tortrices.

The departure of the tortrix larvae does not leave an enormous complex of desirable residences with vacant possession, awaiting new tenants, for this has been a peak tortrix year and they have made a pretty thorough job of defoliating the oak. For a brief period the tree looks as though it had started to strip itself in preparation for winter. The oak, however, is facing a challenge it has met before. It starts immediately to repair the damage. Within a few short weeks it has a new garment of leaves, as tender and fresh as the first crop. Not quite the same, though. At first they are coloured

35

bronze rather than green. The colour change to green occurs as the outer epidermis of the leaves hardens and the chlorophyll factories swing into full production again. With the passing days, many of the other kinds of caterpillar become fully grown, for summer is short and they have to make haste to fit in both the active eating periods and the dormant pupal periods of their lives. Some will remain as pupae through the coming winter, but most will hurry on to the adult insect stage. Emerging as male and female, they will mate in the warm afternoons and evenings of late summer, producing eggs on whose survival through the winter the species relies.

On a day in early July Jim Noyce is accompanied on his routine patrol by a couple of enthusiastic young entomologists, Graham and Jonathan, whose purpose is to collect some of the caterpillars feeding on the oak. They arrive armed with long rods, a sheet and satchels filled with boxes. The sheet they spread on the ground beneath the tree, and with the long sticks they proceed, thoroughly but not too vigorously, to beat the branches. The caterpillars, many of them now nearly fully grown, come tumbling down.

The boys are excited by some of the rarities. Here is a caterpillar of the dark crimson underwing moth, *Catocala sponsa*, 7 centimetres long and closely resembling the knobbly twig along which it has been stretched. So well is it camouflaged that they would never have spotted it by just searching the tree. Its period as a chrysalis will be short, for the magnificent moth, with its crimson and black lower wings and its 7-centimetre wingspan, will be flying in late July and August.

Equally unobtrusive are the caterpillars of the pale oak beauty moth (*Boarmia punctinalis*), which bear a remarkable resemblance to a dead oak twig. When feeding or resting they anchor themselves to a twig by their two rear pairs of claspers and hold their bodies rigid. The boys would almost certainly have overlooked them, but here, on the sheet, are six or seven of them, for they are quite common.

Graham has spotted some small specimens of the pale tussock moth caterpillars (*Dasychira pudibunda*), not long out of the eggs, for these have until the end of September to feed and grow. They are hairy creatures, with tufts along the back like the bristles of a tooth-brush. Their greenish-yellow colour, with black bands between the brushes, blends well with the foliage of the oak. They too are fairly plentiful.

A treasure which produces shouts of excitement from the boys is a lobster moth caterpillar (*Stauropus fagi*). This extraordinary creature does look something like a lobster, perhaps even more like a scorpion. It certainly does not have a familiar caterpillar shape but is an assemblage of knobs, excrescences, lumps and whiskers. Coloured light brown, with its outline broken up by a black line or two, it so nearly matches the bark of the oak branches that it would never have been found without beating.

If there are any newly emerged caterpillars, the boys miss them, which is not surprising for they can easily be mistaken for ants. So they miss the fascinating sight of the young caterpillar, just out of the egg, enjoying its first meal, which consists of its own eggshell. It will take an hour or two over the process. Evidently the shell contains something essential to the young caterpillar, for caterpillars deprived of it die. Each caterpillar eats only its own shell, never the shell of any other caterpillar even of the same species. The mature lobster moth is a handsome, fat-bodied grey creature of quite conventional appearance, in no way matching the bizarre eccentricities of its larva.

Some caterpillars of the blotched emerald moth (*Comibaena pustulata*) puzzle the boys. What they take to be a cluster of scales and leaf-bracts discarded by the oak suddenly starts to move about, revealing a couple of reddish-brown caterpillars which have been deliberately camouflaging themselves. With silken strands they had attached bits and pieces of oak foliage to bristles on their bodies. These caterpillars, unlike most, hibernate and resume feeding in spring, and the specimens the boys find are nearly full grown, having hatched last summer. The attractive green moth has pale blotches and red margins to its wings which make it look as though it is sadly weatherbeaten.

As often happens with dedicated naturalists, a chance bonus comes their way. Walking to the other side of the tree Jonathan happens to glance at the trunk and is astonished to see an enormous caterpillar, 10 centimetres (4 inches) long with a body at least one centimetre (½-inch) in diameter, apparently on a tour of exploration. Its colour is blackish-red on the back and pinkish along the sides, and it progresses with that purposeful stride which indicates that it is searching for a place to pupate. Neither the boys nor Jim has any doubt as to what it is – a goat moth caterpillar.

Jim could hazard a good guess as to where it came from. Beneath the bare, dead branches projecting from the summit of the oak is a stark scrag of a limb on the western side, where once, long ago, a lightning bolt struck. Where the lightning scored a deep scar down the trunk, ripping away the bark, the exposed heartwood has started to rot. Every year the decay penetrates deeper and deeper into the trunk, and eventually, as with so many ancient trees, the Chetham Oak will become hollow. Woodpeckers and nuthatches, attempting to excavate wood-boring insect larvae, assist the work of decomposition. In their search for food they have not been entirely thorough, for they have failed to find the goat moth caterpillar – and not for one season only but for three or four years, the time this insect spends in its larva stage. During this period it

increases its weight no less than 72,000
times. Naturally the vast quantities
of wood it eats earn it the enmity
of foresters.

'Smell it!' Jim commands, and
on doing so the boys wrinkle
their noses in disgust.

'That's how it gets its name. 'It
smells like an old billy-goat.
And you can smell the wood where
it's been feeding for years after
it has left.'

The unpleasant odour probably has a
protective value, deterring birds and animals which might
otherwise try to make a meal of the juicy-looking morsel.

At home the boys take particular care of their handsome
specimen, providing it with a large box and plenty of wood
shavings and rotten wood, in case it needs another meal
before pupating. They are wise enough to place it in a tin box,
for a wood-boring insect such as this would have no difficulty
in eating its way out of a board prison. Within a few days,
however it has contentedly spun a cocoon and turned into a
chrysalis.

The other caterpillars collected are also given suitable cages
for pupation, though their needs are not quite so exacting.
Old-type meat-safes, with sides, front and top of perforated
zinc, make admirable houses for caterpillars and chrysalids,
and several different species can be kept in each. On the floor
it is as well to have a layer of soil covered with dead leaves,
peat moss litter or something similar, for the benefit of insects
which bury themselves underground when they pupate.

A few days later the boys are back again, this time to see the
purple emperor butterflies, which are just emerging. The
purple emperor is one of the largest and most striking of
British butterflies, as well as being one of the rarest. It is
distinguished by being one of the few butterflies to have a
nature reserve of its own – at Blackmoor Copse, Farley, near
Salisbury. Although its caterpillar feeds on sallow leaves the

butterfly itself haunts oak woods, so the ideal habitat is a damp oak wood with numerous clearings and rides and an undergrowth of sallow and hazel. Today several of the butter-flies are flying high around the Chetham Oak, their brownish-black wings suddenly flashing with a brilliant purple sheen as they flutter and display, but none comes as near as the boys would like.

'Come with me again at the weekend,' Jim invites them, when told of their disappointment.

The Saturday afternoon is sunny and warm – just the right weather to bring the butterflies dancing in the glades – but even so the boys are surprised to see eight or ten of them on the ground under the old oak.

'What's that they're feeding on?' they ask.

Jim shows them. The decaying paunch of a rabbit!

'I put it there especially for them,' he confesses. 'For all their loveliness, they like nothing better than something high or stinking to feed on. If I couldn't have provided a rabbit paunch I would have given them a bottle or two of milk that had been standing in the hot sun for a couple of days and started to curdle. They would have liked that just as well.'

A butterfly very like the purple emperor but lacking the purple iridescence is the white admiral, which is found in the same type of woodland and flies at the same season. They are

oak naturally attracts an appropriate quota of insect-eating birds and mammals. The birds tend to be specialists, each concentrating on a particular zone of the great tree. Chiff-chaffs (still, now in summer, occasionally using their monotonous song), wood-warblers, blue tits, great tits and chaffinches methodically quarter the upper canopy. Long-tailed tits, coal tits, bullfinches, goldcrests and willow-warblers generally occupy an intermediate zone. Nuthatches, tree-creepers, greater and lesser spotted woodpeckers and sometimes great tits busy themselves on the trunk. The tree-creepers always start low down and work obliquely upwards; the nuthatches usually work head downwards, like the downlooker flies. Presumably the nuthatches, by approaching their prey from a different angle, find camouflaged insects which the others have missed.

Robins, blackbirds, chaffinches and marsh tits exploit the woodland floor. In the now dense summer undergrowth that encloses the glade, blackcaps and garden-warblers are still engaged in rearing their young, though they no longer advertise their presence by song. Nor does the nightingale, who is also there but whose voice, when he does venture to use it, is now more like that of a choirboy whose voice has broken down into a cracked bass.

On the western side of the oak, where the lightning struck, the hollow which has gradually been eaten out by weather, fungus and woodpeckers is this year occupied by a pair of little owls. They have reared four young, which are now on the point of flying. Last year a pair of stock doves made first claim on the hole, but they evidently succumbed to some hazard during the winter so the little owls were able to move in unchallenged. They have made of it a smelly slum, littered with droppings, pellets, feathers and dismembered bits of carcases. The cleansing activities of innumerable micro-organisms will be needed over the next ten months before the site will be suitable for residence again. Sooner little owls will almost inevitably lose it to aggressive jackdaws who have so far failed to move in simply because they have not yet discovered it.

The upper side of one of the great horizontal limbs of the oak, broad as a highway to a squirrel or a wren, is a favourite perch of a male nightjar, who, after the peculiar custom of its tribe, always sits *along* rather than *across* it. The nightjar is normally a late arrival on migration, not putting in an appearance until the middle of May, and so is still in the middle of its nesting period. All day long the male sits dozing on his branch, while his mate incubates their two eggs in a scraped hollow among dead leaves on the woodland floor, just beyond the edge of the clearing. As dusk closes in he wakes and prepares to relieve her, so that she can replenish her body fuel with the luscious cockchafers, maybugs, moths and other insects that hurtle around the old tree. All that nightjars need to do when hungry is to fly around in the twilight with their mouths wide open. Any insects that blunder in cannot escape because of an inward-facing palisade of bristles which lines its wide gape.

It is dimpsey – a lovely Devonshire word descriptive of the brief period when the lingering twilight is fading into the velvety blackness of a summer night. Two people are walking quietly along a broad ride towards the old oak's glade. They are Grant Noyce, Jim's son, and his girl-friend, Sandra.

They think they have the woods to themselves. They are oblivious of the scores of pairs of eyes watching them – squirrels, wood mice, dormice, deer, foxes, owls, nightingales, warblers, hedgehogs, bats, woodpeckers, blackbirds, rabbits, shrews, robins, woodcock and, of course, the male nightjar. He has been cheerfully unwinding his strange, rattling song since the first stars became visible – that song which has been described as 'whirring', 'churring',

'clicking' and, quite appositely, as an alarm clock going off.

The couple approach the edge of the glade. They are now within five yards of the female nightjar crouched on her nest. Time to investigate.

The churring, whirring song suddenly ceases. For a moment silence reigns. Then Grant and Sandra are startled by an alarming apparition hurtling through the dusk towards them. It is about the size of a football and resembles nothing so much as a disembodied black head with two staring white eyes. The spectre approaches on a bouncing, zigzagging course to within a stride of their faces. And as it comes it utters a loud, metallic clacking – a kind of slow handclap.

Sandra shrieks and clutches Grant. Even Grant, who knows what it is, finds the hairs on his nape rising. The forest depths are an environment stranger and much less hospitable by night than they appear to be by day. Who knows what menacing mysteries may lurk in the darkness? The apparition vanishes. Grant (not Sandra, because her face is buried in the shoulder of his coat) sees the eerie black globe retreating across the glade and vanishing into the gloom of the old oak. A moment or two later the nightjar's clatter is resumed.

What the couple have seen is a typical nightjar display. The male nightjar has been investigating them and advising them that they are on his territory. His flight is naturally erratic, for it is designed to enable him to snap up flying insects en route. When displaying, each of his wings describes a half-circle – an arc of 180° – meeting first beneath the body and then, with a loud clap as they strike each other, above the head. That is the ominous sound they found so alarming. When the wings are flapped rapidly in the gloaming they give the impression of a dark sphere, about the size of a man's head. And prominent on each wing is a white mark which, under these circumstances, look like a pair of glaring white eyes.

There we have the basic essentials of a woodland ghost story, and no doubt they have been responsible for many a one.

Grant reassures his partner and leads her, still shivering a little, across the glade to the base of the oak. There, among the green glow-worm lamps scattered all around, they settle down on the damp grass.

It has been a summer of perfect weather. After a dismal and tardy spring the weather switched to a more cheerful mood in the second week of June. A high-pressure system established itself over the British Isles and, apart from a thunderstorm in early July, held its own against Atlantic depressions until early September.

That thunderstorm was just what was needed to achieve perfection from the point of view of the flora of the forest. It supplied the stimulus needed by the late-flowering plants while doing nothing to damage those which had already switched to producing seed. By midsummer the opportunism of the primroses, violets and wood anemones in flowering so early in spring becomes clearly evident. If they delayed for only a few weeks they would stand no chance. A speeded-up film of forest vegetation in early summer will show a desperate and ruthless struggle for a share of light and space. Frantically the eager species thrust upwards. By early June the croziers of the emerging bracken have expanded into dense jungles of fern five feet or more high, smothering everything beneath them.

Foxgloves achieve success by relying on their tall, stout stems. Honeysuckle twines around every available support and triumphantly opens its fragrant flowers high in the hazels. Brambles attempt to suppress competition by sheer weight and vigour, being capable of producing strong, prickly strands six or eight feet long in a single summer. The woodland rides are lined with tall thistles of several species – the spear thistle, musk thistle, marsh thistle, creeping thistle and welted thistle – all contesting for space with rosebay willowherb, hemp agrimony, hogweed, knapweed and the numerous other flowering plants and shrubs that press forward from the edge of the forest. Drifts of golden St John's-wort have taken over sections of the glades and clearings.

All revelled in that welcome deluge of water poured down from the dark and dramatic heavens. The lightning and thunder, spectacular and exhilarating to humans, were inconsequential background details to them. Nor were the wild creatures of the forest unduly disturbed. As denizens of the outdoors they accept rain, sunshine, wind and celestial pyrotechnics with the same equanimity as they accept day and night. Birds with nestlings huddle more closely on their nests; their mates perch philosophically nearby, holding themselves erect to let the water run off their plumage. Butterflies and moths take refuge under leaves. No-one comes to any harm.

Before the wind that always precedes the rain of a thunderstorm the fragile birches bend and sway, but the sturdy oak does no more than flutter its leaves. Allowing for three thunderstorms per summer, which is a conservative average, it has experienced close on 2,500 of them. Only once in its lifetime, as we know, has it been struck by lightning.

Within a few days of the July storm the soil seemed as dry and parched as ever, as though no rain had fallen all the summer. The plants had benefited, though, and the speed at which they now matured under the hot sun was astonishing. Quickly they allowed their now useless flowers to fade and drop their petals. Fertilisation complete, all their resources must now be devoted to producing seed, their hope of immortality. Although in the depths of the forest and under the shade of the great oak green is still the predominant colour, the grass and herbage of the rides and clearing are drying up like hay. Or like the pale and desiccated grassfields beyond the woodland frontier, where cattle and sheep send puffs of dust spiralling with every step. The distant hum of combine-harvesters and attendant tractors and trailers testifies to the activities of farmers gathering the ripened grain.

By early September the drought is visibly affecting the intermediate forest vegetation as well. The browns, yellows and bronzes of the jungle herbage and foliage form a harmonious background to the ripening berries of wayfaring tree, hawthorn, guelder rose, spindle and the vivid red fruits dangling from festoons of bryony vines. Deer with their fawns seek by day the shade of the deepest thickets where they curl up, panting and tormented by flies and ticks. Birds have long since lost their voices and are in the traumatic throes of losing their feathers. Cold-blooded adders and lizards find the heat much to their liking and provide, with the hordes of biting insects, an effective deterrent to all but the most determined ramblers. Apart from a few devoted entomologists and the conscientious warden, Jim Noyce, such visitors as enter the forest are those who come strolling in the cool of the evening.

A family of them settle for an evening picnic by a lane on the far side of the wood. They eat their sandwiches to the accompaniment of radio music, and the children play and laugh and shout under the trees and through the dense brakes of fern that were made for hiding games. The civilised parents dutifully collect their litter and stow it in the car boot but fail to notice one youngster toss away an empty bottle. It lands on a stone, splits and lays in a tinder-dry nest of bracken. Next day a sunbeam discovers the broken glass, is intensified and concentrated by it. A smouldering frond, a wayward spark, and within minutes the forest is blazing.

Predictably in that thinly populated district, the fire has a strong hold before it is discovered. Once the alarm is raised time has to be allowed for fire-engines to arrive from the nearest town, then, as reinforcements when the magnitude of the conflagration becomes known, from two other towns. Jim Noyce and the boys and all available inhabitants of Chetham and the neighbouring villages turn out with fire-brooms, to fight a losing battle in the heat and smoke. The regimented conifers, which predominate on that side of the forest, fall in their ranks like the expendable soldiers they resemble.

There are three major sorts of forest fires. The commonest is the *surface fire*, which goes racing through the forest, feeding on everything combustible between the forest floor and the tree-tops. In times of severe drought, when the carpet of leaves, fir needles and fibrous roots have been stripped of their moisture, *ground fires* spread actually beneath the forest floor, consuming the top layers of humus. The third and most dangerous type is the *crown fire*, in which flames, sparks or fireballs leap from tree-top to tree-top. Chetham Forest is soon assailed by all three, the initial surface fire soon developing into the other two disastrous types as well.

From a helicopter circling overhead the controller of the fire-fighting operations soon realises that his best chance of controlling the conflagration is to create a fire-break. The most suitable line of defence seems to be a broad ride of which the glade in which the great oak stands is an extension. Bulldozers and men with pick-axes, spades and shovels are set to work broadening the ride and heaping up a barricade of soil. The trees on either side, fortunately most of them young conifers of no great stature, are rapidly felled, to prevent the crown fire from leaping the barrier. Piled up on the near side of the rampart, they are set alight to create a controlled fire, guarded by a battalion of men with fire-brooms. The hope is that by the time the main fire reaches this zone the controlled fire will have consumed everything combustible and will have died down, leaving a belt too wide for the flames to cross.

All day long the battle rages. By late afternoon the main fire has sent out probing skirmishers to test the fire-break defences. From behind the blackened barricade firemen with hoses fight them with water and fire-repellent chemicals. The flames recoil and flicker out, but behind them the roaring furnace still advances. The Chetham people glance anxiously at their great oak, bastion of the forest and now half obliterated by drifting smoke. One fire-engine is diverted to spraying its vast area of foliage, lest it prove to be the vulnerable fingerhold for a fireball fired across the clearing.

As the fate of the oak and the remainder of the forest hangs in the balance, an ally which none of the weary fire-fighters, intensely preoccupied with their tasks, are expecting is about to appear. Over the past day or two television and radio weather forecasters have been talking about an approaching depression, well out in the Atlantic. Inured to drought, no one had paid much attention. All through the summer Atlantic depressions have been following their usual course north-eastwards across the ocean but, diverted by Britain's persistent anticyclone, they pour their rain either on northern Scotland or on the resentful holiday resorts of the Mediterranean. Now, at last, the situation is to change. The anticyclone edges away eastwards, leaving the way clear for the depressions to resume their habitual course. And, as often happens, they herald their approach with thunder – the first

since that isolated storm in early July.

A few cock pheasants on the fringe of the forest hear the first distant rumbles and shout their instinctive challenge, but the fire-fighters are too preoccupied to notice them, even if they could hear them above the crackling flames, the roar of machinery and the cacophony of shouts. But the trees sense that the storm is coming. A breeze sets the topmost foliage of the oak fluttering. Then a sudden gust of wind has the birches bowing and swaying. The fire bellows louder than ever, like a bull deprived of its heifer bride, and makes tentative sallies against the barrier.

At last the men notice the signs. 'The wind! It's changing!' they call.

The smoke which enveloped them begins to pour back into the fire. It is evident now, too, that the blackness of the sky is not entirely due to the smoke; the western half of the sky is indigo, deepening steadily to black. High and beyond the sparks and flames flash the infinitely more powerful discharges of lightning.

'Praise be!' they exclaim. 'We're saved!'

The three inches of rain that fall in the next three hours, followed by the procession of water-heavy depressions that arrive during the next few weeks, effectively extinguish the last embers of the fire and end the long drought. England's weather resumes its normal and monotonous humidity.

Viewed objectively, the fire has done no great harm. It came too late in the year to affect many nesting birds, though possibly a few wood-pigeon squabs perished. Anyone who happened to be on the windward side of the fire could have seen, if they had had time to notice, furtive deer poking tentative noses into the open and then making a dash for safety. Perhaps a fox or two and some rabbits and squirrels retreated by the same route. Resident adders, lizards and slow-worms retired underground, into the holes of mice and moles if they could not find one of their own. There were, however, innumerable insect victims, as could be surmised from the activities of rooks, jackdaws, magpies and jays, foraging in the ashes for a roast breakfast next morning.

Over the stricken area the micro-organism population was, of course, wiped out. In the upper layers of the soil, the decomposing humus and the vegetable detritus of the summer months, the bacteria, algae, protozoans, actino-mycetes, acarina, nematodes, collembola, micro-fungi and the rest, perished in many millions in what must have been, to them, the Book of Revelation become reality – 'The heavens being on fire dissolved, and the elements melted in fervent heat.' For them it was the terrible end of their world. Yet so brief are their lives and so prolific are the myriads of others of their kind that their doom is an incident of little significance.

The black ash, prevented by the saturating rain from dispersing over the countryside, settles down to sodden disintegration. Wood-ash is potash and potash is potassium, which is one of the three major plant foods. New ranks of conifers are planted, and next spring the forest vegetation, as a consequence of the soil's replenished fertility, springs up more vigorously than ever. From the ecological viewpoint the episode was no more than a variation of the eternal recycling of nature's basic materials.

As for the old oak, it stands as immovable as ever. It was lucky. Its fate could have been similar to that of the celebrated Fairlop Oak, in Hainault Forest, Essex, which was destroyed by fire in 1805. After a life of more than a thousand years,

during the latter part of which its shade was the scene of a famous fair to which Londoners flocked, it was set on fire by a party of drunken cricketers.

4

THE OAK IN AUTUMN

1868. November 2nd. Am rejoiced to find that Acorning
has ended for this Season and that nearly the whole of
those absenting themselves on that account have
returned to School this morning, having had a most
bountiful harvest, such a one as the oldest inhabitants
have no recollection.

So reads an entry by the headmaster in the logbook of a
New Forest school.

At this rather late date the acorns were presumably collected for pig food. It may be, however, that even in the 1860s
some of them were ground or pounded into meal for mixing
with wheat flour for bread, an old-time practice for eking out
supplies in times of scarcity.

The subsidiary consideration of collecting acorns so that
young cattle (of which large numbers roam the New Forest)

should not gorge themselves on them must also have been given some weight, for acorn poisoning can cause many deaths among cattle. Acorns which fall, unripe and green, in September have much the same effect on ruminant animals as small green apples do on boys. Eaten to excess and without an adequate corrective of hay, grass or other fibrous food, they are retained in the animal's first stomach instead of passing to the second for normal digestion. Inflammation of the stomach wall develops and deaths are (or were) not infrequent.

The right, exercised in almost every manor in feudal England, to allow pigs into the forests for the autumn harvests of acorns and beechmast was known as pannage. Few if any lords of manors can ever have prohibited the exercise of that right. They were more interested, of course, in the forest deer than in the peasants' pigs, and deer, being ruminants, suffer in the same way as cattle. If the peasants, by pursuing their usual parsimonious customs, deprived his deer of the privilege of committing suicide, that suited the lord of the manor very well.

The right of pannage was exercised from 25 September to 18 November. After the latter date any acorns that remained, being ripe and therefore relatively harmless, had to be left for the deer. Pannage rights were attached to an agricultural holding or farmstead, not to a person. At the beginning of the season the peasant farmer had to notify his lord's steward of the number of pigs he intended to turn loose in the forest, the number of course not exceeding his entitlement. Naturally he had to pay a fee, which in medieval times ranged from about a halfpenny to fourpence a pig. At a time when a mature pig was valued at two shillings, the latter figure is a high one, but it shows the value placed on pannage. It seems that as far back as the Saxon monarchy the fees were adjusted in accordance with the amount of flesh put on while the pigs were in the forest. In those days, before a cash economy became general, the lord claimed a proportion of the pigs as they returned from the forest to their winter quarters. Modern farmers who in quite recent years have had to get used to assessing the quality of their pig carcases by measuring the back fat electronically may be startled to learn that the Anglo-Saxons used precisely the same criterion. They measured the back fat by fingers: three fingers' thickness; two fingers' thickness; a thumb's thickness. The measurements would, of course, be reasonably accurate for slaughtered pigs, but for live ones they could only have been guesswork. Doubtless, however, the lord's steward was the arbiter, and no wise peasant would have ventured to argue with him.

Deer are now the only large mammals left to take advantage of the acorn crop, which is just as well at present, when the acorn crop has been failing through the knopper gall onslaught. Of course, in an autumn when the acorn harvest is good many birds and small mammals gather to the feast. They include jays, squirrels (the grey species, which has replaced the native red one over most of Britain), pigeons, pheasants, rats and several species of mice.

'Prodigal' is the adjective properly applied to the acorn crop. In normal times the great Chetham Oak produces thousands of acorns, most of which are eaten by birds or animals. Of all the acorns borne by the tree in its productive lifetime, only one is needed to replace it when it dies. Only one in more than 800 years! But from those which are carried away and dropped inconsequentially about the countryside by jays, squirrels and the rest a whole forest could grow.

Movement in the woodland in autumn is downward. In spring, life has its ambitions fixed on the heavens. The ascending sun calls and beckons to all living organisms. Now, in the evening of the year, the tired children creep back earthwards to rest.

Acorns tumble to the ground. Replete caterpillars hasten down the oak trunk to bury themselves and pupate in the humus around its base. Thistles, willowherb, ragwort, hemp agrimony, foxglove and all the other tall flowering plants of the woodland, having shed and dispersed their seed by the respective techniques they have evolved, are either with-drawing their resources into the haven of their roots or, if annuals, are sere and dying.

The oak too is preparing for winter. It is stripping for its annual defiance of the gales and blizzards of winter. In spite of its immense strength and the deep anchor of its roots, to try to maintain its huge and heavy canopy of leaves throughout the seven months of siege would impose an intolerable strain. The conifers can cope because their conical shape and the thin, glossy needles of their foliage enable them to shed unduly heavy loads of snow and to filter the buffeting gales, while their habit of huddling together provides protection for the individual trees. The oak disdains such aids to survival but does not go into the ordeal unnecessarily encumbered.

Its leaves, ceasing to manufacture chlorophyll, are losing their green colour, allowing the yellows, oranges and browns that are based on trace minerals in the tree's nutrients to take over. At the junction of the leaves and twigs barriers of a corky substance are being formed, effectively cutting off the supply of sap. Inevitably the yellowing leaves will soon die. Most of them, after a brief display of autumn glory, will flutter to the ground, there to add their quota to the humus for recycling, but on some of the younger trees – not on the old oak whose annual rhythm was long ago developed to perfection – the gum which fastens them to their twigs is too strong, holding them fast all through the winter.

The thunderstorm which ended the summer drought her-alded weeks of rain, a normal feature of an English autumn. Lashing storms saturate the steaming woodland with water drawn from the inexhaustible reservoir of the Atlantic Ocean, while in the brief, sunny intervals the moist, sodden atmo-sphere is fed by drippings from the twigs. In these ideal conditions fungi of almost infinite variety flourish.

The micro-fungi of the soil and the humus layer of the forest floor are, of course, always present (except when temporarily destroyed by fire), but now the secret mycelia of the larger fungi reveal their presence by producing spectacular fruiting bodies. Pliny, writing in the first century AD, was not far off the mark when, in attempting to account for the fungus boletus, he wrote:

> The origin of boletus is from mud and the acrid juices of the damp earth, or frequently from those of acorn-bearing trees; at first it appears as a kind of tenacious foam, then as a membraneous body, afterwards the young boletus appears.

This boletus is a vigorous, plump, handsome fungus with a swollen stem almost as distorted as the trunk of a baobab tree. Its cap is greyish-white, its pores yellow changing to pink, and its flesh is also yellow changing to pink or blue on exposure to air. There are several species of boletus, some of which are poisonous – one even bears the name *Boletus satanas* in reference to its toxic qualities. On the other hand, *Boletus edulis*, known also as cep (in France *cèpe*) is a tasty and much appreciated ingredient of French cuisine, and several other species, such as the orange-cap boletus (*Boletus versipellis*) and *Boletus badius*, which has no popular English name, are also edible. Even *Boletus satanas* is said to lose its toxicity when thoroughly cooked. And the boleti in general seem to be well provided with vitamin D, which is absent from green vegetables. Boletus is an obvious temptation to the gourmet with a taste for experiment, but considerable caution is advisable.

There is, in fact, no universal safe test for the edibility of fungi. The fallacies are numerous.

Fallacy No. 1: Edible fungi peel. Yes, they do, but so do some of the poisonous ones, notably the death-cap fungus

(*Amanita phalloides*).

Fallacy No. 2: Edible fungi will not tarnish or blacken silver. No, nor will non-edible fungi.

Fallacy No. 3: Pick fungi that have been nibbled by rabbits or squirrels or eaten by slugs. That sounds logical but it is unsafe. Rabbits can digest fungi that would be toxic to us, while slugs will thrive on the deadly death-cap fungus.

Fallacy No. 4: Edible (or, according to an alternative version, non-edible) fungi will cause milk to curdle. A useless and completely unreliable distinction.

The only safe procedure is to learn fungus lore from an expert. Let someone else make the potentially disastrous mistakes!

Such an educational course could be well worth while because some of the edible fungi are very tasty indeed. Among those especially associated with woodlands are the parasol mushroom (*Lepiota procera*), found in the clearing around the Chetham Oak and along the grassy rides leading to it; the blue cap (*Tricholoma nudum*), a violet-coloured mushroom of delicate flavour which grows on dead leaves under the tree; the lobster mushroom (*Russula vesca*), a mushroom of the clearing; the prickly cap (*Pholiota squarrosa*), which lives on decomposing bark at the foot of the great oak and is, despite its rough and warty appearance, edible and wholesome; and the inkcap (*Coprinus atramentarius*), which in the course of a single day collapses from a pristine white pixie-cap to a soup of black ink – edible but hardly appetising.

The beefsteak mushroom (*Fistulina hepatica*) can be regarded as the oak's own property, for in autumn it grows from the living wood of its trunk, protruding like great, flat,

59

brownish plates with scalloped edges. Arranged in layers, like steps attached to the bole, they have a glistening, liver-brown upper surface, and a yellow undersurface, and exude a reddish juice, like underdone beefsteak. In spite of their unprepossessing appearance, they are edible, though with a rather strong flavour. Oddly, they taste something like beefsteak.

Another fungus sprouting directly from the tree, though in this instance from the wood of the dead branches, is the oyster mushroom (*Pleurotus ostreatus*). It occurs in clustered masses and has a brownish-black cap with white gills. Fungi of the genus *Mycena*, of which several species are found on the oak, gave their name to the ancient Greek city of Mycenae, whose most celebrated king was Agamemmon.

Of the toxic fungi living beneath the shade of the oak one of the best known and most notorious is the fly agaric (*Amanita muscaria*). A handsome mushroom, it has a bright red cap covered with white excrescences, and its stem is also white. Its name is derived from the fact that it was, and in parts of central Europe still is, used as a fly repellent, for which it seems to be reasonably effective. Folklorists say that in eastern Siberia it is taken as a drug to produce intoxication and hallucinations. Under its influence addicts utter predictions which are thought to be dictated to them by a god or spirit.

The stinkhorn fungus (*Phallus impudicus*), which lives among the bracken at the edge of the clearing, is not poisonous but is so repulsive that one would have to be extremely hardy to attempt to eat it. It starts its career as a roughly spherical 'egg', on the soil surface, much like a puffball but of irregular shape. From this a stem emerges surmounted by what in a mushroom would be a cap but which in the stinkhorn is a bare pileus. From this is exuded a greenish-brown slime with a most appalling odour. If stinkhorn fungi had been ripe when Grant and Sandra settled down at the trunk of the great oak they would quickly have jumped to their feet and moved on. No one would willingly remain within twenty yards of that dreadful stench. Yet, presumably because it is so like rotten carrion, it has a remarkable attraction for flies, which flock to it and remain sipping the slime until they appear to be hopelessly drunk.

The fungi associated with the oak may serve as examples of the infinite variety of uses that can be made of the same materials. In the recycling process one plant may use the nutrients it obtains to produce what are to us aesthetically attractive flowers; another may divert some of its resources to growing protective thorns; another may manufacture poisons; and yet others flaunt properties which cause us to recoil in disgust. But beauty is in the eye of the beholder.

Fungi do not, like flowering plants, produce seed which needs to be fertilised. Their reproductive agent is the spore, of which the larger fungi release prodigious numbers when ripe. An estimate of the number produced by the giant puff-ball is 7,000 million. These spores when they find a congenial environment gradually become elongated and tube-like organs which branch and extend rapidly in many directions. The humus beneath the tree, the soil in which the tree grows, and even the wood of the tree itself are thus penetrated by countless numbers of these strands of fungi, known as mycelia.

Mycelium is a wonderfully efficient collector of nutrients from the soil. From the decomposing plant residues it extracts carbohydrates and proteins, with which it produces, at the appointed time, the fungi which we see. Experiments at Rothamsted Experimental Station have shown that where fungi are the cause of the familiar dark-green fairy rings in grassland the eventual loss to the pasture, by cutting or grazing the grass produced, amounts to 11,500 lb of carbon and 740 lb of nitrogen per acre. What the mycelium does is bring these elements to the surface where they can be harvested and removed. Under our oak, however, when the fungi fruit and die their residues are devoured by bacteria and absorbed into the abundant life of the soil, and so the eternal cycle continues.

Edible mushrooms do not grow in the clearing around the oak, as they much prefer open grasslands. However, the commonwealth of the oak does include one invisible fungus which, though now little known or regarded, once had a considerable economic value. It is the truffle (*Tuber aestivum*), an undistinguished-looking lump of black fungus ranging in size from a walnut to a teacup. It grows underground, as much as three feet deep, beneath forest trees, especially the beech and the oak.

Truffle hunting was, until early in the present century, a recognised occupation for woodland folk in districts where the fungi were sufficiently plentiful. In England the truffle hunters were generally led to them by small dogs, specially trained to search them out. From earliest puppyhood, the dogs' food was smeared with truffle. The dogs naturally associated the scent of truffle with food and became adept at finding the fungi. Local tradition alleges that the 'truffle hounds' were introduced by a Spanish exponent of the art probably in the seventeenth century. At one time it proved a useful subsidiary industry for groups of independent cottagers in winter. So important was it to one Wiltshire village in 1860 that the villagers sent a petition to Parliament requesting exemption from the annual dog tax of twelve shillings, on the grounds that 'being poor labouring men, living in a woody district of the county where there is a great many English truffles grow, which we cannot find without dogs, we do therefore keep and use a small pudle sort of dog wholy and solely for that and no other. . . . It has been carried on by our ancestors for generations without paying tax for the dogs.'

Truffles are, of course, highly valued by gourmets. They are still extensively exploited in France and Italy for flavouring pâté de foie gras, truffle-flavoured chocolates and suchlike delicacies. In those countries peasants employ trained pigs and goats to locate them, though apparently neither animal needs much training. In Périgord, one of the strongholds of the truffle industry, some of the truffle diggers maintain that they need no animal assistants, for they know from long experience the trees under which the truffles grow.

Recent research indicates that truffles may also be a kind of aphrodisiac. They have been found to contain a male sex hormone in about double the concentration of that in the blood of a boar. When a boar is sexually aroused it is this substance, androstenol, which pours into his salivary glands, exciting him still further and also producing a receptive reaction in the sow. When the sow discovers the same scent underground quite naturally she immediately starts rooting for it. It is said that she can smell truffles fifty yards away.

Not long ago an English scientist set up an experiment to see whether androstenol had a similar effect on humans. A group of men were shown pictures of attractive girls and asked to place them in order of beauty and sex appeal. They were then exposed to androstenol and asked to repeat their findings. Most of them apparently gave the girls much higher ratings for sexiness the second time round, which was taken to show heightened awareness on the part of the men.

Were the generations of Chetham couples who made love under the great oak stimulated in any way by the presence of truffles beneath them? The idea seems fantastic, but modern research has discovered stranger associations.

Whether truffle hunting was practised in England before the alleged introduction of the trained dogs from Spain is unknown. Possibly lecherous pigs revealed the secret to some perspicacious peasants. Or possibly the delights of the truffle were unknown or unappreciated in medieval England. They were certainly known to the ancients, being referred to by Theoprastus (372–286 BC), by Pliny (AD 23–79), by Martial (AD 38–104) and by others. In mythology they were dedicated to Venus and were supposed to make men more virile and women more amenable. Strange. One would suspect that someone had noticed something. In England, however, the first mention of truffles occurs in 1673, when it is recorded that they were found at Rushton, Northamptonshire. It so happens that there are also records of trees from south-western France having been planted in the same locality not many years earlier, so there is at least a chance that truffles had then been accidentally introduced with the soil. Some seventy years later, though, Gilbert White speaks of truffles as common around Selborne and also near Andover, and he mentions a truffle hunter who called on him.

Wild animals as well as domestic ones naturally appreciate the scent and flavour of truffles. Deer, rabbits, squirrels, mice and badgers are attracted by them, so presumably truffles might be discovered by observing the activities of these animals in appropriate localities in autumn. Truffles are also host to tiny yellow truffle-flies (*Helomyza*), which hatch from the ripe fungus and emerge to dance, like mating midges, over the subterranean truffles on autumn days. I once managed to locate truffles by lying flat on the ground so that I could see the flies, dancing about a foot above the ground, against a clear sky.

Acorns and truffles were not the only woodland harvests of importance in former times. Autumn saw the Chetham villagers arriving in crowds to collect hazel-nuts, much as present-day families flock to pick-your-own strawberry fields. Hazel was the standard underwood of oak forests. A Dorset observer, writing in 1818, says:

The woods consist chiefly of hazel, which produce nuts in great profusion, to the relief and benefit of all the hamlets and villages for miles around. It is their second harvest; for when all the corn hath been got in, and the leasing in the fields at an end, the inhabitants betake themselves to the woods; whole families from distant places flock [thither]; bring their little cots, provisions, utensils and every necessary for their comfort that they can provide themselves with, and make their abode there for whole weeks at a time if the weather will permit. Fuel they have at hand in great plenty; and after the fatigue of the day they make large fires, which they sit round, eat their scanty meal, then slip from the green shells their day's gathering, talk over their success, cracked their jokes as well as their nuts and, clothed with innocence and simplicity, are much happier than most of the Princes of Europe. . . . The neighbouring towns, particularly the sea-ports, are a sure and ready market for their wares, and the price is generally on a par with wheat, the same kind of weather being most favourable for the growth and increase of both.

For some reason few hazel-nuts now stay on the bushes long enough to ripen. Perhaps the once dominant red squirrels did not strip them while still unripe and soft-shelled, as the grey squirrels do. The woodland harvests more in demand are those of blackberries and sloes, the former for making jam and jellies, the latter for flavouring sloe gin. Earlier generations of village housewives also valued valerian, which grows along the woodland rides. The roots were dug up and sold to druggists for medicinal purposes. Cow-wheat was also collected for its medical value, but the rather rare spurge-laurel was dug up and sold to nurserymen for grafting related varieties of mezereon, a practice which doubtless made the species even rarer. Sloe-picking in those days was not the present decorous occupation engaged in by rural or suburban housewives who pick the fruits individually and carry them away in cans or baskets. Whole families used to assemble for the harvest, the men cutting off great boughs or whole bushes, while women and children sat around, picking the berries into buckets. Chemists were ostensibly the main market for the sloes, but I believe that even more found their way to brewers and wine-merchants, for adulterating port wine.

Once or twice during autumn and winter a hunt invades the forest. The hounds come bounding through the undergrowth and careering along the rides, followed by pink-jacketed huntsmen and such of the followers as have been able to keep up the spanking pace. The followers are more numerous than ever they have been, reinforced by increasing numbers of pony-riders, mostly female, who live in suburbanised villages. Possessing a pony is for some an unmitigated luxury, for others a status symbol, for others the realisation of a dream. Joining the local hunt is a 'done thing'.

Fewer foxes than formerly are caught, however. The principles of nature conservation having taken root, rural inhabitants are divided into pro- and anti-hunting schools, while the neutrals, in an emergency, tend to betray a latent sympathy with the fox. Jim Noyce, son of a gamekeeper, has been known (though not by the huntsmen) to divert the hunt deliberately away from the well concealed den amid the roots of the great oak, where he was well aware that the hunted fox had taken refuge.

The huntsmen who assembled beneath its shade when the Chetham Oak was in its prime would have regarded with contempt their twentieth-century descendants chasing such an insignificant quarry as a fox. They were after worthier game, deer – and not those lesser examples of the Cervidae, the introduced fallow and roe, but the noble red deer. Though now often regarded as a mountain species, owing to its having found its last sizeable refuge in the Scottish Highlands, the red deer is primarily a forest animal,

66

and in the immense forests which once covered most of England it attained considerably greater stature and weight than its mountain descendants.

Chetham Oak, Chetham Forest, Chetham village and all the woods and villages for miles around were then included in a royal forest, to which the draconian forest laws introduced by King William applied. In a well-known passage a Saxon chronicler lamented that William 'made large forests for the deer and enacted laws concerning them, so that whosoever killed a hart of a hind should be blinded. As he forbade killing the deer, so also the boars, and he loved the tall stags as if he were their father.' In fact, the Conqueror did not 'make' forests in the sense of planting trees; what he did was to decree the limits of those areas where the forest laws were to be observed.

The new legislation bore hard on independent peasants who had been accustomed to regarding the wild animals of the forest as their legitimate perquisites, though there had been large royal forests subject to rigorous laws before William's time, and the inhabitants of these were experiencing nothing new. In fact, although the laws were there as a powerful background deterrent to misbehaviour, they were not uniformly applied. After all, the king needed people in his forests, to act as beaters, to look after the hounds and hawks, to repair the fences, to cut firewood, and to carry out the numerous other essential tasks on a forest manor. It was not in the king's interest to depopulate the region, but just to keep everyone in order. The code therefore usually operated by a system of demotion. A freeman caught red-handed killing a deer lost his freedom; thenceforth he was downgraded to the status of villein or peasant tied to the land. For the same crime a villein was either imprisoned or demoted to be a bondsman or serf. But a serf similarly convicted could not be reduced in status any further, seeing that he was the lowest of the low, and so he was executed.

Nor should the monarchs who made and administered the forest laws be regarded as inexcusably cruel or arrogant. Firmness was essential and savage punishments were commonplace, but the kings were not acting solely in defence of their own sport or pleasure. Wherever the king happened to be was the administrative capital of the kingdom, and as he moved around his realm his court accompanied him. So numerous were his retainers and officials that they could not stay long in one place. The local provisions soon gave out. So the king and the court moved from royal manor to royal manor (or to the manor of a too-powerful noble for whom bankruptcy was expedient), feasting on whatever the land provided. As a respite from a winter diet of salt pork and leathery beef, venison was extremely welcome and must have accounted for a big proportion of the meat eaten by the king and the royal family. A peasant who killed one of the king's deer, therefore, was not only interfering with the royal sport, he was robbing the king of a dinner.

Many contemporary illustrations of medieval deer hunts seem to indicate that the deer were pursued by hounds, with huntsmen following either on horseback or on foot. There is reason to suppose, however, that often the hunt was organised much on the lines of a modern pheasant shoot, with lines of beaters driving the deer towards sportsmen concealed in the undergrowth. The method would have had the advantage of being selective. The hinds could be allowed to double back through the line of beaters and escape while the stags were driven on towards the royal bowmen. This was almost certainly the system employed on that fatal August day in the year 1100 when William Rufus met his death by an arrow loosed from the bow of a still unidentified assassin.

Note that the Saxon chronicler differentiates between the deer and the 'tall stag'. Like all his contemporaries, he would have been familiar with the technical names given to deer of various ages and types. A *stag* was officially a male red deer in its fifth year. In its sixth year it became a *hart*, and in its seventh and thereafter it was a *great hart*. Before that it had been a *staggard* in its fourth year, a *spayard* in its third, a *brocket* in its second, and before that a *calf*.The female red deer started life as a *hind calf*, became a *hyrsel* in her second year and was thereafter a *hind*.

With fallow deer both male and female began as *fawns*. In its second year the male became a *prickett*, in its third a *sorrel*, in its fourth a *soar*, in its fifth a *buck* and in its sixth a *great buck*. Females were of less importance. They became *teggs* in their second year, and from the third year onwards were *does*.

Complicated though all this sounds, contemporary woodlanders, beyond much doubt, would have been able to identify and correctly name the deer they encountered.

Red deer are indigenous to Britain, but fallow are reputed to have been introduced by the Romans. Roe deer, now the most numerous deer species in England, were once native but became extinct, at least over much of the country. Such stock as survived was reinforced by introduction by private land-owners, notably in Dorset, in the early nineteenth century. Most nights roe deer steal like ghosts under the canopy of the oak, pausing to nibble grass in the clearing, but three cen-turies or more have passed since the last tall stag sought its shelter.

To the statement that in autumn the movement of life in the woodlands is downwards there is one important exception. Autumn is the season of spiders. They abound everywhere. A walk through the woods on a dewy or frosty morning reveals every bit of foliage, from the dry grass-stalks and the sere thistle stems to the topmost twigs of the oak, swathed and festooned with gossamer.

The spinners of much of this silken drapery are refugees. They are escaping from their own mother and their own siblings, cannibalism being rife in the spider world. The spider population of the countryside has been proliferating all the summer until now it has reached the level of more than two million per acre, perhaps more in the woods. In spite of the current abundance of insect and microscopic life, all those spider appetites take a lot of appeasing, and competition is fierce. In their search for a less congested environment, spiderlings have every incentive to disperse. They will be lucky to find an unoccupied niche, for spiders are plentiful everywhere, but they must at least try.

They have at their disposal an almost unique mode of travel. On quiet, sunny autumn mornings, blessed by a gentle breeze, each little pilgrim spider will take a firm hold on the highest perch it can reach, such as the tip of a twig, the top of a fence-post or a grass-stalk, and start spinning silk. The lengthening strand will wave and billow in the breeze, but the spiderling will persevere in its task until the strain is more than it can contain. Then it will release its hold and drift away, supported by the gossamer. Over where it is going it has no control at all. Each spider aeronaut is in the same predicament as balloons released at carnivals. It may be taken aloft and carried for many miles, or it may plummet to earth after travelling a few yards. The webs clinging to the woodland trees, bushes and undergrowth are mostly the parachutes of spiderlings whose odyssey came to an early end, though some may have arrived from distant parts. When the wind is favourable, however, the little aeronauts can make prodigious journeys. They have been found floating on air currents at altitudes of over 14,000 feet and hundreds of miles out to sea.

Spiders have no idea of direction and location, and they have no means of knowing how long they have been aloft or how far they have travelled. When their bed of gossamer catches on some obstruction and is held fast they do not know or care where they are. Their one thought is of food. So the incessant pursuit of prey is resumed, some species of spider actually hunting while others lay their appropriate snares and traps. Were it

70

not for all these spiders the earth would be overrun by proliferating insects and would become uninhabitable for man.

But spiders themselves live hazardous lives. From the moment of birth they are in peril not only from their own kind but from every insectivorous creature of the countryside. For in this context the term 'insect-eating' includes 'spider-eating'. So in the autumn sunshine the great oak is again the haunt of foraging bird companies, hunting spiders. With the native tits, chaffinches, robins, blackbirds, starlings, wrens and the rest, fattening up in preparation for the winter, are now parties of migrating birds, building up their strength for their long journey to Africa. Flycatchers, chiffchaffs, willow- and wood-warblers, blackcaps and perhaps a redstart or two drop in for a few days, as at a caravanserai, to enjoy the abundance of food offered.

For nearly eight hundred years the great oak has been a staging-post on the tremendous journey. Nearly eight hundred generations of small feathered migrants have known that here they could be sure of reasonably safe lodging, complete with food supply. Now it has become programmed into their genetic inheritance. Their inbuilt sense of direction and location brings them instinctively to it. In the distant future when the oak is no longer there (for all living things must die) new generations will intuitively arrive at the site, seeking the food and shelter which instinct tells them should be there.

5

<u>The Oak In Winter</u>

The Abundance of autumn merges almost imperceptibly into the austerity of winter, and just as gradually the woodland settles down to its winter routine.

The Chetham Oak itself has now shed the last of its leaves and is securely fortified against any battering the winter may bring. Next year's leaves and flowers are already formed in embryo but are safely sealed beneath millions of waterproof bud-scales. The impressive hydraulic system that at other seasons raises nutrients in solution from rootlets to twig-tips has closed down. The tree is sleeping.

The ivy on the oak bole is still green. Like the holly, the yew and the conifers, it possesses glossy, pointed leaves which shed snow and water. Like them, too, it does shed its leaves, but not all at once, in autumn. And, like the oak, it has its next year's buds already formed and neatly packed away at the base of the current crop of leaves.

The ivy is one of the latest of all flowering plants, opening its green flowers from October to December. In a mild autumn they provide a much appreciated feast of nectar for surviving wasps, bees, flies and, at night, certain moths. On sunny afternoons in late autumn, ivy flowers hum with life. When this last repast of summer is over and the insects have departed, most of them to die, the ivy berries, slowly ripening during winter, are an important item in the winter diet of berry-eating birds such as blackbirds, thrushes and the migrant fieldfares and redwings.

Paying tribute to another aspect of the ivy's ecological importance, the Forestry Commission states: 'An essential component of the best woodland habitats in Britain, ivy provides the only evergreen shelter in winter.' Certainly the ivy on the oak is well populated in the winter months. Its choice as a hibernaculum by brimstone butterflies has already been noted. For roosting wrens, tits and tree-creepers it offers near-ideal lodging for the nights. By day a tawny owl has selected it as its perch. For a bank vole which has its lair under the debris at the foot of the oak the ivy forms a useful staircase

giving access to the upper storeys of its home, with their interesting food possibilities. Snails cluster in the depths of the ivy for hibernation, sealing themselves in their shells with a lid of hardened slime, though in mild spells they are able to dissolve the casing and venture out in search of food.

Other members of the commonwealth of the oak that are more conspicuous in winter than in summer are the mosses and lichens. About 1,200 species of lichen have found a place on the British list, and a good proportion of them have been recorded on the bark of the oak. Generations of boy scouts have been taught that moss grows on the north side of a tree-trunk – a useful aid to path-finding, or orienteering as it is now called. By and large, it can be accepted, though it is not invariably true. The proximity of other trees and bushes in a forest can have a moderating influence. Where they are close together trees fifty or a hundred years old may bear no moss at all. Lichens grow most profusely on the side of the trunk exposed to the prevailing wind and rain.

 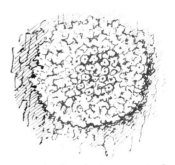

Lichens are strange plants. They are, indeed, integrated communities in themselves, for they consist of certain algae and fungi living together in a mutually advantageous partnership. The fungi contribute mineral nutrients while the algae provide carbohydrates and compounds of nitrogen – a truly remarkable example of symbiosis. On the oak the mycelium of the fungi penetrates the bark and supplies anchors for the colony, while the surface organs of the lichen collect dust and other small particles from the air and break them down into their constituent substances.

Lichens were formerly among the woodland crops collected by country people for sale to merchants who had city markets for them, chiefly among makers of dye. *Lecanora pallescens*, for instance, which was known as crottle, yields an orange or red dye; *Xanthoria parietina*, a conspicuous golden-yellow lichen, was frequently used for dyeing wool yellow; *Parmelia perlata* gives a brown dye; *Pertusaria communis* is a source of oxalic acid and, when treated with iodine, produces a fine blue colour.

The medicinal properties of some of the lichen species were naturally not neglected by our rural ancestors. One common species, *Sticta* or *Lobaria pulmonaria*, which favours the rough bark of old oaks, was given the name 'lungs of the oak', chiefly, it seems, because when properly stewed or infused it was held to be a cure for lung diseases. This species also was used by dyers, producing an orange hue. *Evernia prunastri*, or oak moss, a shaggy grey lichen which grows on oak trunks in humid districts and even on twigs, is still widely used in the manufacture of perfume. The long-tailed tits of Chetham Wood visit the oak every spring to collect beakfuls of this lichen for nest-building. A powdery yellow layer in the cracks of the oak-tree bark will probably be the mustard powder lichen (*Lepraria candelaris*). Old man's beard (*Usnea florida*) resembles the feathery fruits of the traveller's joy, also commonly known as old man's beard. In the days when gentlemen sprinkled their hair or wigs with perfumed powder, this lichen was one of the prime ingredients of the Cyprus powder, in common use for that purpose.

Many lichens are exceptionally sensitive to pollution, though others are less so. Scales have been devised to determine, by study of the local species of lichen, the approximate levels of sulphur dioxide in the air. The old oak, in its secluded clearing, is fortunately in a clean-air zone, otherwise half its lichen population would disappear.

Lichens are the first plants to colonise a bare surface – rocks, brickwork, stone or the fresh bark of a young tree. When they die their decomposing bodies provide a foothold for mosses. Among the early colonists are the *Dicranella* and *Dicranoweisia* mosses, which form bright green cushions on the damp base of the oak, a habitat they eventually share with one of the commonest of British mosses, the greater matted thread moss (*Bryum capillare*). The flat *Neckera complanata* has an extensive colony on the shady side of the oak bole, while another pretty thread moss, *Mnium hornum*, has gained a foothold on the decaying wood which will eventually result in the oak becoming hollow. Competing with the grasses of the clearing are prolific growths of the fernlike *Cirriphyllum piliferum* and *Pseudoscleropodum purum*, while on half-buried rotten branches beneath the oak colonies of *Eurynchium praelongum* wait to take over when at last the grand old tree itself finally succumbs.

Most of the abundant life that exploded around the oak in summer and autumn is still alive, though some of it not as active as it was. With all the proliferating myriads of micro-organisms in the soil and in the layer of decaying leaves and other vegetable debris which covers the soil are the eggs, larvae and pupae of an almost infinite range of insects, spiders, woodlice, worms and other small fry. To study the life in a leaf-debris sample, scoop up a shovelful or two into a sack and take it home for investigation. Empty it on to a white cloth and go through it piece by minute piece. The quantity and variety of life it contains is often astonishing.

This is no surprise to the creatures that depend on the life in the leaf-debris for their own survival. Even in midwinter the wood-mouse (alias long-tailed field-mouse), the bank vole and the shrew are as active as ever – the shrew has to eat three-quarters of its own weight in food each day in order to survive. They spend most of their time in the debris zone, below the dead leaves but above the surface of the soil, though they also use shallow burrows in the earth. A heavy snowfall is beneficial rather than otherwise, for it adds another protective layer against the cold. Under snow in the forest small rodents and insectivores can carry on their activities unhindered.

Predatory animals know they are there, of course. The teeming population around the base of the oak is subject to fairly regular raids by weasels, stoats and foxes. The foxes listen to and sniff out the rodents as they scurry about under the leaf cover, but the weasel, not much larger than its prey, pursues them into their fastnesses. Nor are the denizens of the towering ivy safe from weasel and stoat, both animals being able to climb well. It has been estimated that these two pirates (with occasional help from one or two others) kill off four out of every five hibernating dormice every winter. Under the sheltering branches of the oak the small animals of the leaf-mould zone are safe from the hovering kestrel even in winter, but the tawny owl who sleeps by day in the ivy takes his nightly toll. Prowling rats can at times be a menace, though these prefer to stay nearer human dwellings in winter, if possible. Marauding magpies, crows and jays sometimes come probing for whatever they can find under the leaves. Fat grubs, chrysalids, worms and insects in any shape or form are what they hope and expect to dig out, but a tasty mouse or vole does not come amiss.

The grey squirrels who are wintering in a drey they have built in the angle where one of the largest branches joins the trunk of the oak have few enemies except man. Foresters regard these squirrels as pests because of their propensity for eating the green buds and tips of trees, stripping bark and raiding birds' nests, but, as the nests they plunder probably include those of the even more destructive jays, magpies and crows, they should perhaps be allowed a few credit marks, apart from which they are, as we have noted, almost the only control of the knopper gall at present available.

Contrary to popular belief, grey squirrels do not hibernate, although sometimes in very cold weather they remain huddled in their dreys for a few days. Squirrels of both sexes and all ages may share the warmth of a winter drey, which is more solidly built than the summer dreys and is well lined with dry grass and moss. From January onwards, however, breeding begins, and when a pregnant female squirrel takes over a drey everyone else has to turn out. She will tolerate no other squirrel in the nest with her babies and will sometimes chase away any who venture into the same tree. Another popular fallacy is that squirrels store acorns, nuts and other food against the winter. Certainly they bury nuts and other titbits in autumn, though singly and not in large caches, but

77

they promptly forget where they have buried them. In winter they locate buried nuts by scent (a feat which is impossible in time of snow) and dig them out, but the nuts are not necessarily those which they themselves buried.

So far I have not mentioned the badger sett beneath the trunk of the great oak, except to say that now and again a hunted fox takes refuge in one of the side corridors. The sett, though not quite as old as the oak, measures its existence in centuries. Many generations of badgers have used it, returning to it again and again, despite savage expeditions against it by Chetham villagers in the uncivilised past. Now it is one of the treasures of Jim Noyce's domain, safe under his vigilant protection. At this season the badgers, though not technically hibernating, are drowsy and disinclined to venture outside except in mild weather. Having accumulated layers of fat in autumn, they can if necessary go without food for twelve or fourteen weeks, though they enjoy an occasional snack. At present, however, the sow badger has other things on her mind. Her cubs are due to be born in February, and, eight feet deep beneath the oak, in a cavern protected by its mighty roots, she has prepared a bed of moss and dried grass cosy enough for a human baby.

As winter drags on food becomes progressively scarce, though less so below the soil than above it. Years when acorns, berries and beechmast are plentiful are providential; years when the woodland crops fail bring famine winters. The small birds which remain in Britain throughout the winter or seek a haven here from the even grimmer climate of northern Europe congregate in gypsy bands which circulate around the woods. An observer has only to remain stationary in one spot in order to see the entire population of small woodland birds conducting their activities around him. They travel quickly, snapping up whatever their sharp eyes manage to spot but not working the territory thoroughly.

After all, they will be back again in a few hours' time or tomorrow, and it would be foolish to exhaust the food supply on any one circuit. They do not stick so strictly to their specialised zones as in summer.

The tree-creepers still perform their ritual searches of the bark, working obliquely upwards, but most species concentrate on the woodland floor, knowing that that is where most food is likely to be found. Some of them, however, notably the tits, like to take a titbit to a branch to eat it.

The winter woods now are much quieter than in the days of the old oak's youth, or, indeed, even fifty or sixty years ago. For winter used to be the busy season of the year in the woods for men.

Within living memory a scatter of old men could be seen on winter mornings, trudging along the paths that led to the forest. They were mostly elderly men with whiskers, doubled up with rheumatism or hernias. They wore corduroy trousers fastened below the knee with leather straps ('yarks' is the technical name), and they carried two sticks. One was a heavy walking-stick to help themselves along; the other, supported by a shoulder, carried the weight of a rush basket bearing their lunch and billhook. They were the underwood workers, a moribund race, off to their coppicing in the woods.

The purpose of coppicing was to supply rods of wood for the demanding rural economy of those days. The most skilled of the underwood workers were the hurdle makers who wove from supple hazel rods the wattle hurdles required in vast quantities by the sheep farms. Other underwood products were bean-rods (for sticking runner beans), pea-sticks, faggots (of kindling wood), bavins (bundles often of prickly brushwood for burning whole in bread-ovens and limekilns or for special purposes such as fenders for protecting quays from the bumping of ships in port) and tool handles. Ash poles were in demand for the sides of ladders and for clothes'-posts, though in earlier times they were much valued for the shafts of spears. Birch twigs were bound together for the heads of brooms and doubtless, too, for schoolmasters' birches; black willow was required for the teeth of hay-rakes.

In the deciduous woodland predominant at that time the woodlanders contracted with the estate owners to buy by the acre the cutting rights to underwood seven or eight years old.

They were required to clear everything, except incipient trees, left at the rate of about twenty to the acre, to burn everything for which they could find no use and to leave the place tidy. One can imagine the woodlanders of the early years of this century deploring the passing of the good old days when brambles, which now had to be burned, could be peeled and sold to dressmakers as the foundations for crinolines!

Complementary to the coppicing of hazel, ash and the other underwood was the pollarding of the forest trees themselves. This involved cutting them off at about head height when young and thereafter trimming off the new rods which sprouted from the truncated bole when they were eight years old or so. The purpose was the same as with coppicing, namely to acquire a supply of green rods for numerous country crafts. Those crafts included the construction of wattle-work for wattle and daub, that most popular of primitive building materials. Almost every town and village in England can show examples of it, especially in interior walls, which, plastered over, have endured for centuries.

Most forest trees were subjected to pollarding, even oaks. The great Knightwood Oak, in the New Forest, reveals, on close examination, that once, centuries ago, it was pollarded. The gnarled and ancient Burnham Beeches on the Chilterns owe their distortion to pollarding, as do the hornbeams of Epping Forest. Limes, alders, elms, sycamores, poplars and willows were all given the treatment, and it seems to have done them no harm, for some of the oldest surviving trees were once pollarded. Pollarded trees have decided attractions for birds and for other forms of wildlife. The trunks of trees pollarded within living memory are swollen, eight feet or so above the ground, to great, gnarled knobs, pitted with holes – ideal nesting sites for stock doves, owls, jackdaws and even wild duck. Foxes have been known to sit in them calmly watching human activities below. However, the Chetham Oak escaped. It has never been pollarded.

Pollarding and coppicing were almost certainly practised in the Bronze Age, perhaps even earlier. Eel stages constructed some six thousand years ago near the point where the River Bann escapes from Lough Neagh, in Ulster, are of wickerwork almost identical to that in use for the same purpose today. But the men engaged in coppicing and pollarding in Chetham Forest in medieval times were only a fraction of the total woodland labour force. The traffic around the Chetham Oak in its prime was at least equal in winter to that of a busy farmyard, perhaps to that of a busy market.

Note the imperious gentleman who, on this winter day at the end of the thirteenth century, is sitting on horseback under the oak, attended by three or four retainers. He is the chief forester or warden of Chetham Forest. He is a far more exalted personage than Jim Noyce, the present warden, for he has charge of everything that goes on in the forest and is responsible only to the king. His remuneration is in proportion to his responsibilities. Richard Done, a contemporary of his who was chief forester of the Forest of Mara (or Delamere) in Cheshire, was entitled to:

two strikes [? bushels] of oats at Lent from every tenant for provender for his own horse; bracken at times save the hunting season; pannage and agistment of pigs; windfalls and lops of felled trees; crabstakes and stubs; half the bark of felled trees; all cattle and goats taken at non-agistment times; ½-penny each, and the same of straying beasts between Michaelmas and Martinmas; all sparrow-hawks, merlins and hobbies; all swarms of bees; the right shoulder of every deer taken in the forest; the horns and skins of every 'stroken deer' found dead; waifs [presumably of deer] found in the forest; the hunting of foxes, hares, cats, weasels and other vermin with hounds of greyhounds and the *pelfe*, or best beast, of any that committed felony or trespass in the forest and fled for the same, the lord having the residue.

No doubt the chief forester passed on some of these perquisites to underlings, in return for financial or other considerations.

Under him the chief forester has numerous officials, engaged in the administration of the forest. Bureaucracy is not a modern invention. High in the hierarchy are the *verderers* (there are still verderers in the New Forest) who are supposed to represent or look after the interests of the forest freeholders, though they are appointed by and are responsible to the Crown. This is not an age of democracy. Under these exalted officers, who receive no pay and who are supposed to collect no perquisites but who no doubt need no lessons in the art of feathering their nest, are the *foresters*, who have responsibility for the deer in a defined section of the forest, usually referred to as a 'walk' or 'ward'. Their duties are particularly onerous during the 'fence month', around midsummer, when the hinds are dropping their fawns and must on no account be disturbed, but foresters are supposed to be on duty at all times. In winter their duties include the cutting of evergreens and twiggy branches from high in the trees as food for the deer. They must also ensure that their charges have water to drink, and they must always keep their eyes open for poachers. They are not popular with the forest freeholders, who are obliged by law to give board and lodging to them and their horses and dogs whenever they demand it. Their demands are not always tactful or considerate.

In late Saxon times a *woodward* was appointed in many parishes to control the exploitation of the woodlands, which were even then beginning to be depleted. It was his duty to supervise the cutting of timber and underwood, the lopping of branches and the rights of pasturage and pannage, making sure that no peasant turned loose in the forest more than his proper quota of animals. By the end of the thirteenth century, however, which we are taking as our point of reference, the woodward is a Crown official in charge of the king's deer on a private estate, of which there are quite a number, within the confines of a royal forest. The welfare of the deer is paramount, and the woodward is required to see that no unauthorised tree-felling, building construction or underwood operations interfere with it.

His former responsibilities for controlling the pasturage, pannage and other rights of the forest dwellers are now taken over by an *agister*. Peasants are much addicted to diverting into the forest more cattle, pigs, ponies and other animals than they are entitled to, and the agister is supposed to see that this does not happen. He also has to collect the appropriate payments from the peasants. Another unpopular man!

In some parts of the forest the owner of private property, often an ecclesiastical establishment, has the right to erect a fence to enclose it. The fence, however, must not be too high for a deer to leap over it, for the king still retains hunting rights over the whole forest, regardless of any other claims. His deer still have priority over everything else, and within the private estates he has yet another set of forest officials, the *parkers*, to make sure that this is properly understood and honoured.

Under the suspicious eye of all these forest officials the forest peasants go about their daily business. In midwinter most of the ploughing of arable land is finished or else is impossible because of frost and snow, so the greater part of the village population is in the forest. The *swineherd* is here, with his herd of short-bodied, hump-backed, bristly pigs,

rooting under the trees. So thorough and energetic are these animals that they must have taken a drastic toll of the small mammals and insect larvae and pupae that in the twentieth century winter in the leaf-mould layer. To suppose that the wildlife of the woodlands was richer, more varied and more abundant in early times than it is in our own century is probably a fallacy.

The forest is neatly divided into sections, many of them enclosed by fences of wattle hurdles which, as with private parks, have to be low enough to allow a deer to jump over them. In these enclosures the underwood, mostly hazel, is at various stages of growth, from one to eight years. The eight-year-old stands are being cleared by skilled craftsmen with billhooks, who slash off the straight and supple rods a few inches above ground level. Some are weaving wattle hurdles; some are selecting and trimming straight poles for tool handles, weapon handles, fencing stakes and building accessories; some are gathering brushwood into bundles and binding them with twisted hazel or willow bonds. Pollarded trees in the various sections are being given similar treatment, according to their stage of growth.

Ripe timber is being felled, for building material. Great trunks are being shaped and loaded on to low-slung timber carriages for transport to distant sites or to the nearest river. The king, to whom it all belongs, may well have given a grant of a score or two of massive trunks to an abbey thirty miles away. Teams of pony-like horses are being lined up to drag the huge loads along forest tracks and atrociously rutted lanes to their destination.

In the cold winters prevailing in the Middle Ages the peasants are preoccupied with the problem of obtaining sufficient food for warmth and cooking. Some of them have rights of *estover*, which means the right to cut or gather certain types of wood. Some can collect only *wyndfallen* wood, which consists of branches split from standing trees by wind, heavy snowfall or lightning; others are confined to *rotefallen* wood, which is the small wood from uprooted trees. The trunks of such uprooted trees, known as *cablish*, are forbidden to peasants; they are the property of the Crown or its representative. Groups of drab-clad women in the forest clearings are exercising their rights of *turbary*; they are cutting turf for fuel. Here a man and his wife are loading a handcart with thorn-bushes, which are all he has a right to. Others are cutting bracken for bedding for themselves and their livestock. A goose-girl wanders about with her honking flock. They often follow the pigs, to dispute with them the titbits unearthed by the latter's snouts, though they need to be alert, for a half-savage pig is as liable to grab a goose as anything else. Striding or riding through the busy throng or watching from the wings are the forest officials, ensuring that no one has more than his or her entitlement. It is in their interest to be vigilant, for if they catch a peasant in some misdemeanour they can 'attach' some of his goods and chattels. Theoretically these are forfeited until the next attachment court, held once every forty-two days; but even if the peasant is found innocent (which is unlikely) he will be lucky to get them back.

The outer boundaries of Chetham Forest are marked by a deer leap, a deep ditch from which the excavated soil is piled on the outer rim to form a rampart, like a defensive ditch around a town. The rampart is crowned by a high hurdle fence, and the combination of ditch, bank and fence make it impossible for a deer to stray. Keeping this barrier in good repair requires the services of a gang of men throughout the winter months. Within the forest are other, smaller, enclosures constructed in the same fashion, with high wooden gates to admit the deer as desired. These enclosures are known as 'buckstalls'. Here in hard weather the deer are fed with twigs and evergreens and even hay when any is available. The Chetham Oak often has its outer branches trimmed for the purpose. The buckstall also offers the advantage of deer penned sufficiently closely to be snared without the trouble of hunting, when one is required. In medieval forests the practice of farming deer, considered in the twentieth century to be a novel idea, is highly developed.

Fulke de Castiard, the chief forester, astride his horse under the great oak, is bilingual. When speaking with his social equals he uses Norman French but when shouting at the peasants Anglo-Saxon. Some of the peasants understand a smattering of the court language but all use Anglo-Saxon among themselves. Though to our ears much of their speech would be unintelligible, many of the names are not. The peasant with the handcart is Dick Yeates. The woodward reporting to Fulke de Castiard is John Gay. The goose-girl is Amelia Titt. Among the gang engaged in repairing the deer leap are Tom Purkess, Harry Puttock and Gilbert Shakeshaft, whose descendant would, under the amended name of Shakespeare, raise the amalgam of the two languages to a pinnacle of golden glory. But the present Gilbert Shakeshaft toils with shovel and bidle and mutters curses on the overseer in basic Anglo-Saxon.

Less reputable characters also dwell in the forest. Deep in the unclaimed fastnesses of the old forest, as far away as possible from Chetham and other villages, old Simon Brock, the hermit, has his filthy cell. A mile or so away, in equally unsavoury conditions in a cave, lives Gaspard the leper. And somewhere in the forest, though no one knows where, Robin Noyce, the outlaw, has his lair. Robin is a longbowman, and was with the Crusaders. Having enjoyed wider horizons than those of Chetham, he has not found it easy to settle down to the routine of peasant life now that his overseas adventures are ended. To be more precise, he has made free with the king's deer once too often, and now he is an outlaw – outside the protection of the law and liable to summary justice if ever he is caught. Not that that worries him at present. He is well able to look after himself.

Betrayed in the end by a girl, Robin Noyce was eventually strung up on one of the horizontal branches of the great oak, neither the first nor the last to meet a similar fate. The oak quite frequently bore strange fruit from its mighty limbs in medieval times. It would have borne more if Robin had revealed the involvement of Simon the hermit, Gaspard the leper and sundry Chetham peasants in his nefarious activities, but he died silent.

A woodland industry which had greater prominence in the thirteenth century than today was charcoal-burning. From the beginning of man's mastery of ironworking techniques, charcoal has been in considerable demand, and for centuries was an essential item in the all-important trade of making arms, armour and armaments. Later it was an ingredient of gunpowder and was also in demand by glass-makers. Eventually many ancient forests, especially those clothing land where iron ore was present, were largely denuded of trees to meet the incessant demands. The Weald of Kent and Sussex, for instance, possessed in the early seventeenth century no fewer than 80 furnaces and 90 forges, all producing and working iron and all requiring quantities of charcoal.

Charcoal-burners, or collyers, to give them their ancient name, were a race apart. From necessity they had to live with their work, for charcoal hearths must be tended day and night. They lived in temporary huts close to their hearths and probably kept nocturnal watch by rota.

The hearths were built in a clearing, such as that around the Chetham Oak, which must have seen many of them in its time. Each hearth was about five yards in diameter and stood about five feet high. It was made of split logs, each a few inches in diameter and about four feet long, up-ended around a central stake about six feet high. The logs were arranged in a sloping pattern around the stake to form a dome which, when complete, was covered with a layer of straw and then with other layers of turf and soil. A further layer of logs was then added and this too was covered deeply with soil and leaves. When all was ready the central stake was pulled out, and into the 'chimney' thus formed burning charcoal was dropped, together with a few lengths of kindling wood to give the fire a start. Once the fire was well alight, the chimney was sealed and the charcoal-burners settled down to watch.

A hearth burned for five to ten days, during which time the charcoal-burners had to be constantly alert, day and night, especially towards the end of the process. On no account had the fire to be allowed to break out, for the essence of charcoal-burning was that the wood has to be consumed in the virtual absence of oxygen. A sudden change in the wind direction could speedily bring the danger of a flare-out and send the charcoal-burner frantically piling more earth on the threatened section. Or he would quickly move ready-made straw-covered hurdles to form a screen. When the fire had eventually died down and experience had told the charcoal-burner that the burning was complete, he broke open the hearth and raked out the charcoal, taking care that none of it burst into unwanted flame. When cool, it was shovelled into sacks for transport.

Of course, several hearths at various stages of combustion would be burning at the same time, while others were being prepared, so the charcoal-burner's operations would be continuous as long as the local supply of wood lasted. When it was finished he would move to another site. He was peripatetic, travelling over a wide area and spending all his life in the woods.

The many kinds of wood had their own special uses in the making of charcoal. Oak, alder and sweet chestnut were considered most suitable for refining iron, while birch, beech and willow were in general use. The charcoal sticks now used for sketching are generally of willow. Charcoal-burning was in general a summer task, but during the winter the charcoal-burners found plenty to do, cutting and splitting their cordwood and preparing sites for the summer work.

Charcoal-burning is still a thriving industry, but not in Britain. Only a handful of charcoal-burners are now at work here, and these use metal kilns instead of the old-type hearths. Most of the 300,000 tons or so of charcoal that annually find their way into the world market are produced in the tropics, where much more is also produced and used locally without ever being recorded.

Some country folk maintain that they have seen ghostly evidence of old-time charcoal-burners. When a hearth was fired it first sent up clouds of billowy white smoke and then settled down to producing a blue, lazily spiralling haze. On warm, tranquil afternoons in late summer, say the witnesses, ghostly blue thermals, emanating from long-dead hearths, can be seen rising above the tree-tops in places where the charcoal-burners once worked. 'Collyers', they call these apparitions. The smoky spirals are, in fact, clouds of dancing gnats, like the truffle-flies, though it seems a shame to spoil a good story.

On an August day in the year 1100 the bleeding corpse of William Rufus was carried from the place of assassination in the New Forest to Romsey Abbey in the cart of Purkess, the charcoal-burner. New Forest is still the home of the Purkess family, just as Chetham Forest is of the Noyces. Tenacious families, these forest folk.

Yet another peasant specialist who would have been seen about his business in medieval woods was the bee-ward. Bees had a much more important role in the rural and indeed the national economy in the days when honey was virtually the only sweetening agent, though, in fact, it was prized even more as the basic ingredient of mead. Enormous quantities of beeswax, too, were required for the candles used in religious ceremonies.

> 'Bees, o bees of Paradise,
> Sang the praise of Jesus Christ,'

wrote a medieval poet, adding that without bees (in their capacity of wax-makers) there could be no Mass.

In the thirteenth century the era of the straw bee-skep may have lain ahead. Hollow logs were probably used as beehives, as they are in Africa today. In winter the bee-ward would be exploring the deeper parts of the forest for suitable logs for summer use and for suitable trees on which to hang their occupied hives, though they must always have had the hope that they would find a hollow tree with a swarm of wild bees in residence.

The busy, noisy scenes enacted around the great oak nigh on seven hundred years ago have vanished for ever. The shouts and the shrieks and the songs have died down. Silence has descended on the winter woodlands, and Jim Noyce, visiting the oak on his daily patrols, seldom sees another human in the woods between November and March. The exceptions occur on four days when a syndicate, exercising shooting rights for which it pays a useful sum towards the upkeep of the forest, organises pheasant shoots. Then for a few brief hours the woods echo to the reverberations of gunshots and to the cries of beaters. It is a traumatic experience for the denizens of the forest, but much less so than the forest fire, and the visitation is soon over. Peace returns, and the life of the woodland resumes its normal tenor.

6

History And Folklore

Foresters DO NOT now come in autumn to collect ripe acorns for planting in their forest nursery. This year they might, in any case, be unlucky, the knopper gall onslaught having all but wiped out the acorn crop. The knopper gall should, however, prove less of a menace to the oak than Dutch elm disease did to the elm, for it does not kill the trees. It merely prevents them from reproducing themselves, and seedlings can readily be supplied from unaffected sources. Geneticists are busy with the forest trees, as with every other living species, selecting the best and most efficient specimens as parents for future generations. The pollen-proof polythene covers with which they protect their selected female flowers from unwanted pollen should also keep the knopper gall-flies away from the flowers of the oak. The pollen from the chosen male flowers, which bloom before the female, can be stored until the females are open and receptive and can then be blown into the plastic protective sleeves. Once the female flowers are pollinated, the covers can be removed.

To grow oaks in a forest nursery acorns are sown, in well prepared soil or in seedbeds of conifer litter, in drills about 1 inch deep and 4–6 inches apart, the acorns being about 1½ inches apart in the drills. They are covered lightly with fine soil and need to be well protected against marauding mice, squirrels and birds. One pound of acorns will produce about seventy young oak plants. After one or two years the seedlings are ready for transplanting, each one being given about twice as much space as before. Forest nurseries are now devoted mainly to conifers, these being the trees for which there is most commercial demand. They are a more economic crop to grow than hardwoods because they grow much more quickly and so produce an earlier harvest. In practice, new plantings are thinned at intervals, the final stand of spruce being reduced eventually to about 50 per acre. In Britain conifers are often used as nurse crops for hardwoods of much greater longevity. Lines of oaks, for instance, planted between lines of conifers will take over after the conifers are felled. In new oak plantations, a rarity now, the young trees when about 24 inches high may be spaced at 4 feet by 2 feet, giving a total of 5,450 per acre, to be reduced by thinning as they grow until they finally stand at about 20 per acre.

Such sophisticated management is relatively new. Our Chetham Oak owes its existence to chance. In an autumn when Henry Plantagenet was king of all England and about half of France as well, a squirrel (a red one) ran off with an acorn from a mature oak in Chetham Forest and was about to shell and eat it when it was disturbed by a marten. In panic it dropped the acorn, which fell into a patch of mud and was, that very night, squelched into the soft soil by a passing deer. Perils innumerable attended its early years, but somehow it survived them all.

The process by which a forest perpetuates itself without human intervention is known as natural regeneration. It still prevails in many of the world's forests and was unchallenged in England until a few centuries ago. Until the great rural estates embarked on programmes of landscape planning, after the wholesale enclosure of land by Acts of Parliament, not many forest trees were deliberately planted. Why interfere with a natural process which had worked satisfactorily since time immemorial?

A few thoughtful and far-sighted persons viewed with some anxiety the rapid denudation of England's forests in time of war. Towards the end of the fifteenth century it became evident that they were a wasting asset, a realisation that resulted in the first Act of Parliament (1483) regulating the management of woodland. With the increasing demand for timber for shipbuilding, James I commissioned a detailed survey of some of the country's chief forests, including the New Forest, where the commissioners found between 60,000 and 100,000 mature oaks. One of the first plantations of which there is any record was made in Windsor Great Park by Lord Burleigh, who in 1580 sowed some thirteen acres with acorns and fenced them in to keep out deer and cattle. By 1625 a forester reported that it had grown into 'a wood of some thousands of tall young oaks, bearing acorns and giving shelter to cattle, and likely to prove as good timber as any in the kingdom.'

An early champion of the need for growing timber for the navy was John Evelyn, the diarist, who in 1664 wrote a book on silviculture, in which he declared that 'all arts and artisans whatsoever must fail and cease if there were no timber and wood in a nation. . . . We had better be without gold than without timber.' His argument is a reminder of the extent to which England, and indeed all other European countries, relied on its trees in the centuries before the use of metals was fully developed. Evelyn was a popular writer whose recommendations were soon being extensively put into practice by landed gentry. Charles II set an example by establishing in the New Forest a forest nursery of 300 acres devoted entirely to oak seedlings.

The demand for timber increased rather than declined. By Nelson's time no fewer than 1,000 mature oaks were needed to build a ship of the line. Some steps towards meeting future requirements were taken soon after the Restoration when, in addition to establishing his forest nursery, Charles II decreed that 1,400 acres in the New Forest and 11,000 acres in the Forest of Dean should be replanted, mostly with oaks. By the eighteenth and early nineteenth centuries most private land-owners were managing their woodlands with some degree of efficiency, cutting ripe timber at regular intervals and replacing felled trees by new plantings. At the same time, however, many estates were augmenting their farmland at the expense of their forests, so the result was a net loss of woods.

Recent research has indicated that the nation's reserves were, in fact, more than adequate, in spite of all the anxiety about them. At the time of the Napoleonic wars England's forests still covered more than a million acres, which was about ten times the area needed to maintain in perpetuity a navy the size of Nelson's. The situation was rendered even easier by the resumption, by the 1830s, of large-scale imports of oak from Mediterranean countries, and soon afterwards the development of the iron and steel industry and the building of iron ships reduced for ever England's dependence on her home forests. Thereafter forestry languished, its prosperity being closely linked with agriculture, which, except in wartime, was in almost permanent depression from 1875 to the 1950s.

The study of pollen reveals that as the glaciers of the last ice age receded trees took over the vacated land probably in the following order: dwarf willow; then birch; then pine, accompanied by much hazel; then, by about 5000 BC, other forest trees, notably oak, elm, ash, lime and alder.

Two species of oak established themselves in Britain at this time and may therefore be regarded as native. They were *Quercus petraea* (formerly *sessiflora*) and *Quercus robur*. The former, sometimes called the durmast or sessile oak, bears its

acorns on very short stems but has
long stalks to its leaves.
Quercus robur, sometimes known as
the pedunculate oak, has short
leaf-stems but carries its acorns
on long stalks. The durmast oak,
the only native oak in Ireland, is
thought to have colonised Britain
first, but the pedunculate oak
probably arrived not much later.
The pedunculate oak is now probably
the commoner of the two. Some oak
trees are intermediate between the
two and seem to be hybrids.

Other oaks now growing in Britain but all introduced
within the last two or three centuries include the turkey oak
(*Quercus cerris*), the holm oak, also known as the ilex or
evergreen oak (*Quercus ilex*), the American willow oak
(*Quercus phellos*) and several species of American red oaks,
among them *Quercus rubra* and *Quercus coccinea*. As a matter of
fact, the American red oaks appear to do better in England
than in their native country, where their height seldom
exceeds 70 or 80 feet while in England there are several
examples of over 100 feet.

In prehistoric and early historic
times the oak was the
predominant tree in the great
forests which covered much of
Europe, including Britain. It features
very prominently in the religions
of the Celts, Teutons and Slavs. The
priestly caste of the Celts are familiarly
known to us as Druids, which is said to
mean 'men of the oak', being derived
from an Indo-European root whose
ramifications appear in the word for oak in
Greek (*drus*), in Gaelic (*darach*), in Irish (*dair*) and Welsh
(*derw*), in the Sanskrit word for wood (*drus*), and in durmast

97

oak. *Dryw*, the Welsh word for wren, correctly suggests that the bird is intimately associated with the oak in Celtic folklore. Innumerable place-names in Celtic or former Celtic regions bear testimony to the cult of the oak. Examples in Britain include Stanton Drew (a Somerset village with prehistoric stone circles), Cerrig-y-Drudion (in Wales) and Inis Druineach (Iona) in Scotland; also the English river names Dart, Darent and Derwent. In Ireland, oak names include Derry, Kildare and possibly Tara, the meeting-place of the ancient high kings of Eire, where a great oak once stood. In Asia Minor the ancient Galatians, a Celtic people, had as their religious centre a place called Drynemetum, 'the sacred grove of the oak'.

In the Celtic calendar the oak gave its name to a month – Duir – which covered the period from 10 June to 7 July. In this calendar the year was divided into thirteen months, each of 28 or 29 days and measured from one full moon to the next.

Similarly in Anglo-Saxon the word 'oak' is derived from the root word 'ac', discernible in 'acorn' ('oak-corn') and 'acre' (said to derive from the fact that most small fields, reclaimed from virgin forest, had an oak-tree in them). In England it can be detected in such place-names as Oakley, Oakwood, Oxshott (once Oakshott), Acton (of which there are at least 24 examples), Akenham, Accrington, Oakhill, Oakfield, Oakham, Oakhanger, Wokingham and Savernake.

In Roman and Greek mythology, Jupiter (or Zeus), the father of the gods, was also the god of the oak and of thunder, attributes shared by the Norse god Thor. The association of the oak with thunder is thought to derive from the loud cracking and groaning that emanate from a great tree when it is felled. As John Aubrey, the seventeenth-century antiquary puts it: 'When an oak is felling, before it falls it gives a kind of shriekes or groanes that may be heard a mile off, as if it were the genius of the oak lamenting. . . . To cut oak-wood is unfortunate.' A similar association links the woodpecker with the oak, the bird's drumming being held to resemble thunder.

Celts, Teutons and Slavs all worshipped in oak groves like the one at Drynemetum in Galatia. The sacred grove at Dodona, in Epirus, celebrated all over the ancient world for its oracles, transmitted by priestesses, was of oak trees. In Greek mythology the dryads were, in essence, the spirits of trees, living and dying with their trees, originally oaks. In Plataea, also in Greece, once in five years an offering of meat was placed in a grove of oaks and carefully observed to see in which of the trees the local ravens first perched when they had helped themselves to portions. The tree thus favoured was felled and fashioned into an image. In a jubilee festival at the end of sixty years all the accumulated idols, dressed as brides, were collected and burned in a great holocaust of sacrificial animals.

Slavonic peoples of eastern Europe worshipped, under various names, a deity similar to Jupiter/Zeus. In the great medieval market of Novgorod stood an image of the thunder god, Perun, whose sacred tree was the oak. Nearby a school of priests kept eternal vigil over a sacred fire of oak wood, on which from time to time oxen were sacrificed. Should a priest inadvertently allow the fire to be extinguished, he was doomed to be sacrificed there when the fire was rekindled. The people of ancient Estonia likewise worshipped an oak god whose name was Taara, making an annual sacrifice of oxen with whose blood the oaks were anointed.

The significance of sacred oak groves to peoples living in

the forest regions of Europe was well understood by early Christian missionaries, more than one of whom issued his challenge to the pagan gods by cutting down a sacred oak. Patrick did it in Ireland; Boniface was martyred when attempting to do it in Frisia. Sometimes, however, the old traditions were simply taken over by the Church. That must have happened at Kildare (a place-name which means 'the church of the oak') where until as late as the sixteenth century the nuns of St Brigit kept a perpetual sacred fire burning – a fire which must originally have been kindled not to the honour of St Brigit but to that of the decidedly formidable pagan goddess also named Brigit. And St Columba stepped in on one occasion to prevent the felling of the sacred oak grove at Derry.

Oak groves were evidently the scene of the ritual slaying of the priest-king, a feature common to several ancient religions. At the appointed time his successor would seek him out in the sacred grove and kill him. In some instances it seems that his body was then consumed on a pyre of wood from the oak tree which was held to be possessed by his spirit. The killing by an arrow of William Rufus at Lammastide (1 August) in the year 1100 is held by some authorities to have been just such a ritual sacrifice of a god-king of a pre-Christian religion of which Rufus was a secret adherent. It is not widely remembered that early in May of that year (Beltane, or May Day, being in the ancient Celtic religion the quarter day that preceded Lammas) Richard, a nephew of Rufus, was similarly killed by an arrow in the New Forest. Was he offered as a substitute sacrifice which was not accepted? Was it deemed necessary for the real king to die on the next quarter day? Even as late as 1538 a man described as a priest was brought to London from Wales, together with an idol carved from oak, which bore the same name as himself, and both were burned at the stake at Smithfield.

The reputed Druidic reverence for the association of the oak and the mistletoe is well known. It is, of course, rare for mistletoe to occur on oak. The apple is the tree usually parasitised, and some authorities have wondered whether there has been some confusion between the two trees.

100

However, in the days when oaks were a hundred times more numerous than they are now it is conceivable that mistletoe was found on them more frequently, and Pliny, who gave the first account of the ritual, stressed that the occurrence was even then rare. When mistletoe was discovered on an oak it was reverently cut with a golden sickle by a high priest (the Arch-Druid) so that it fell into a white cloak held by other priests. Two white bulls were then sacrificed to the god of the oak, and prayers were offered to him for renewed fertility of flocks, fields and herds. The belief seems to have been that mistletoe berries were the semen of the oak and therefore extremely potent magically.

Centuries after Christianity became the official religion of England, country couples used to celebrate their marriage under an oak. Eventually the Church forbade it, but even then the couple would go from the church service to dance three times around the oak as ancient custom decreed. No doubt this was a ceremony often witnessed by the Chetham Oak.

So the old pre-Christian customs and traditions lingered long, and even now they have not been entirely forgotten. One of them now anchored on Oak Apple Day has already been described. Originally it must have belonged to May Day (the Celtic Beltane), which before the adjustment of the calendar in 1752 was eleven days later than it is now. Recent years have seen widespread revivals of May Day festivities, which include dancing around the maypole, morris dancing, the bearing of garlands and the enthronement of a May Queen and sometimes a May King. These two characters, of which the King was the more important, were spirits of nature – now, in the month of May, being revived by the strengthening sun. The King was a tree spirit, the spirit of the oak, and appeared on May Day clad in oak greenery. By medieval times he had become known simply as The Green Man, or Jack-in-the-Green, or sometimes he was even transformed into a chimney sweep. In some stories and traditions he can be identified with Robin Hood, Maid Marian being the May Queen. An old couplet, still remembered, declares:

'Fairy folk
Live in old Oaks.'

101

The May Day celebrations were unashamedly fertility rites, appropriate to the season of the year, and the Maypole was undoubtedly a phallic symbol. The couples who stole away on the eve of May Day to make love under the Chetham Oak understood that quite well.

The eight or nine hundred years attributed to the Chetham Oak is by no means unique. In Windsor Great Park stands the Conqueror's Oak, reputed to have been a large tree in William the Conqueror's time and much admired by that monarch. It would thus appear to be not less than 1,200 years old. Only the shell now remains, the main trunk having collapsed about a hundred years ago, but it still produces foliage every spring. The Polstead Oak, which stood in Polstead Hall Park, Suffolk, is in a worse state of decay, though quite recently it was still living. A Gospel Oak ceremony is said to have been conducted under it for a thousand years. The Carmarthen Oak is reputed to have been older, for it is associated in local tradition with Merlin, King Arthur's magician in the sixth century AD.

> When Merlin's oak shall tumble down,
> Then shall fall Carmarthen town.

So the people of Carmarthen have encased it in concrete and put railings around it, but it is now only a dead stump.

Probably the most famous oak in England is the Boscobel Oak, in which King Charles II hid from Roundhead soldiers after being defeated at the Battle of Worcester (3 September

1651). It grew in the grounds of Boscobel House, Tong, Shropshire, and was a pollarded oak. As it had been trimmed three years previously it had sent up a dense thicket of shoots from its crown, and in early September these would have been densely covered with leaves, providing excellent cover for the fugitive. Imaginative pictures of the youthful Charles (who was then aged 21) sitting astride a great branch or curled up in the fork of one are incorrect. The present Boscobel Oak is believed not to be the tree in which Charles took refuge, that one having been literally chopped to pieces by souvenir hunters. This present one is said to have been grown from an acorn produced by the authentic Boscobel Oak, as are several other venerable trees in various parts of the country, but an element of doubt exists.

When Charles was restored to the throne, amid great rejoicing and general relief, the episode of his narrow escape at Boscobel caught the popular imagination. May 29th, the date of his restoration (and also, incidentally, his birthday), was established as Oak Apple Day, a public holiday which attracted to itself many of the ceremonies and customs formerly attached to May Day but suppressed under Puritan rule. It was considered the patriotic duty of everyone to wear a sprig of oak-leaves on that day, various penalties being exacted on those who forgot or refused to sport the token. At Torquay, Devon, where punitive customs were observed as late as the 1880s, boys and girls carried bunches of nettles for chastising any delinquents. In East Anglia and Cumbria hair-pulling was often substituted for the nettles, while in Sussex the day was commonly known as Pinch-bum Day – said to refer to the fact that, when they were hiding in the oak with the Parliamentarian soldiers all around, Captain Carless, the king's companion, had to keep pinching him to keep him awake. Other traditions are that the king climbed into the tree by means of 'a hen-roost ladder' and that while in the oak he released a wood-pigeon he had carried with him for that purpose, to fool the pursuing soldiers that no men were hiding there – a questionable notion! As time went on and Oak Apple Day became more and more confused with May Day, Charles II became in some places identified with The

ROYAL OAK

Green Man.

Charles II was not the only monarch to hide in an oak. His father, Charles I, had a similar adventure when escaping, disguised as a servant, from Oxford in 1646. The oak which concealed him still survives and is known as the Big Oak. At Irton Hall, Holmbrook, Cumbria, is a hollow oak in which King Henry VI hid after the Battle of Muncaster (1464), during the Wars of the Roses. The tree still stands in the grounds of a school.

An oak known as the Rufus Oak stood for centuries on or near the spot in the New Forest where King William Rufus was killed by an arrow in the year 1100. Naturally the oak was said to be the one which deflected the arrow into his body, but that is doubtful. An obelisk, known as Rufus's Stone, now occupies the site. Hoxne, in Suffolk, had an oak, still standing in 1846 or 1847, reputed to be the one to which King Edmund the Martyr was tied and shot to death with arrows by Danish invaders in the year 870.

Several ancient oaks bear the name 'The Queen's Oak'. Under one of them (also known as The Northiam Oak), by the village green at Northiam, Sussex, Queen Elizabeth I dined on 11 August 1573 on her way to Rye. The same story is told of the Crouch Oak, at Addlestone, Surrey. The Queen's Oak at Huntingfield, in Suffolk, was also favoured by a visit from Queen Elizabeth, who once shot a buck under it. And under another, in Hatfield Park, the same queen sat on 17 November 1558, reading a Greek testament while waiting for the news of the death of her sister Mary and hence of her accession to the throne. She was supposed to have been caught kissing the Earl of Leicester under an oak in Gorhambury Park, Hertfordshire, the tree being thereafter known as the Kiss Oak. Honour Oak, a London suburb, takes its name from the Honour Oak under which this same Queen Elizabeth dined in 1602. Under Fairmead Oak, in Epping Forest, King Henry VIII waited to hear the guns of the Tower of London announcing the execution of his Queen, Anne Boleyn.

Numerous oaks are understandably associated with executions, their great horizontal limbs naturally lending themselves to hanging. On the Abbot's Oak, Woburn, the Abbot of Woburn and several of his clerical colleagues were hanged for defying the orders of Henry VIII regarding the dissolution of religious houses and also for criticising the condemnation of Anne Boleyn. Several oaks in the West Country were used for the execution of prisoners condemned by Judge Jeffreys for supporting the Monmouth Rebellion. At least six of Monmouth's men are said to have been strung up on the Heddon Oak, near Crowcombe, on the Quantock Hills of Somerset, a handsome tree with some massive branches obviously suitable for gallows. Forty years earlier an East Anglian Royalist, Sir John Rous, hid for three days in a hollow oak in the grounds of his estate, Henham Park, in Suffolk. The tree had previously been used as a summer-house and had been fitted with a door covered with oak bark, which proved completely effective camouflage.

The Headcorn Oak, in the Weald of Kent, reputed to be well over a thousand years old, has in recent years been thoroughly renovated and reinforced and looks good for a few more centuries yet. Local courts were once held under it, and local tradition says that it was the scene of bull-baiting contests staged for King John. At Meavy, Devon, the Royal Oak has likewise received the attentions of skilled tree-surgeons, who have removed all the dead wood, treated it with fungicide and given adequate support to its time-heavy branches. This tree too is said to have associations with King John, and it was certainly a Gospel Oak.

It was also one of those remarkable Dancing Trees, which were a feature of a number of old-time Devonshire villages. Sabine Baring-Gould write of it, in the 1890s:

> This tree till within this century was, on the village festival, surrounded with poles, a platform was erected above the tree, the top of which was kept clipped flat, like a table, and a set of stairs erected, by means of which a platform could be reached. On the top a table and chairs were placed, and feasting took place.

Other species of trees besides oaks were converted into Dancing Trees, but the oak seems to have been the favourite. A certain landowning family held its land on the condition of dining once a year on top of a Dancing Tree at Dunsford. At Trebursaye, in the same area, the dancing was discontinued when a woman fell off the platform and broke her neck. Thereafter her ghost haunted the place until exorcised by the rector of Launceston. At Lifton when the Dancing Tree fell down its memory was perpetuated in the name of the local inn, the Royal Oak. This Lifton Oak was reputed to be always the first in the district to come into leaf. In this respect it resembles the Cadnam Oak, which, as a matter of fact, is in the New Forest village of Copythorne, not Cadnam. For many years it has unfolded some of its leaves on 6 January (Old Christmas Day), though producing the main leaf-crop at the usual season. People used to make long journeys to see this remarkable event, sometimes

106

holding midnight parties on the eve. The Forrard Oak, at Witley, Surrey, is said to have a crop of leaves by mid-March in most years. The reason for this curious behaviour is not known; perhaps the trees in question are aberrant hybrids.

The idea of a platform on a flat oak-top seems natural enough when we think of a pollarded tree. For several years when my children were small I had a tree-top house for them on the top of a pollarded oak. Such trees also naturally lent themselves to use as look-out posts. At Linkinhorne, in Cornwall, the hollow Darley Oak had seven stone steps inside it, leading to a look-out post on the top. Another oak at Chertsey, Surrey, also has steps leading to a former tree-top platform.

The village of Cressage, a name which derives from 'Christ's Oak', is thus named after an oak tree. One old oak there, in the last phase of its life, is said to be the tree under which St Augustine preached in the year 598, but other trees in the Welsh Border counties make a similar claim. One is the Rock Oak, at Rock, Worcestershire; another the Mitre Oak, still standing at Hartlepury, in the same county. The Great Oak of Oxford, alternatively known as the Magdalen Oak, is alleged to have been planted when Alfred the Great founded a college there. It was old enough and large enough to be called the Great Oak when William of Waynfleet founded Magdalen five hundred years later. Selly Oak, the populous suburb of Birmingham, takes its name from a huge old oak, the Selly Oak, which flourished until early in the present century and was then cut down, despite determined local opposition, to make room for a new development scheme.

Gilbert White, the father of English natural history, makes special mention of two oaks in the vicinity of Selborne. One was the Raven Oak, so called because from time immemorial it was the nesting-site of a pair of ravens, until the tree was felled and the birds killed. Under the other, the Pleastor Oak, on the edge of the village playground (the 'pleystow'), the village children played and the older folk sat and gossiped on summer evenings – the natural and commendable function of a village oak.

Turnpike Oaks are often examples of eighteenth-century opportunism. The turnpike roads that were established at that time generally followed the lines of existing roads or tracks, whose surfaces were improved. Large and ancient trees were often to be found on the margins of old roads, and where these happened to be hollow they saved the turnpike trusts the necessity of erecting toll-houses for their toll-keepers. And some enterprising characters were shrewd enough to occupy convenient hollow trees and attempt to collect tolls where none were due!

Several ancient oaks situated near highways have claimed associations with Dick Turpin, the highwayman, and have appropriated the title Turpin's Oak. One was at Thirsk, Yorkshire; another at Bedfont Green, Middlesex; another at Finchley; and a fourth at Haileybury College, Hertfordshire. The Finchley Oak, which survived until about the middle of the nineteenth century, had a bole large enough for the highwayman to hide behind it when he was waiting in ambush. At Mugglewick Common, in county Durham, a farmer named Pedom, who augmented his income by sheep-stealing, used to hide the stolen animals inside a massive hollow oak, which was consequently known as Pedom's Oak. Of Hankford's Oak, Monkleigh, near Bideford, a grim story is told. Early in the fifteenth century the estate on which it stood belonged to a Lord Chief Justice of England, who, having had trouble with deer-stealers, told his gamekeeper in exasperation to shoot at sight anyone who failed to give an agreed password when challenged. Not long afterwards the gamekeeper shot the judge himself who, forgetting the arrangement and the password, was strolling one evening under the oak.

It is probably not generally known that Birnam Wood, which plays a key role in Shakespeare's *Macbeth*, was an oak wood. It was situated on the south bank of the river Tay, near Dunkeld, Perthshire, but the last oak died not many years ago.

Another remarkable oak wood is Wistman's Wood, on Dartmoor. Among a scatter of granite boulders on an acid, exposed hillside some 1,400 feet above sea level, the gnarled and distorted trees which comprise the wood cower close to the ground and are embedded in ivy. They are incredibly old. A ring count of one only seven inches in diameter in the 1860s proved it to be no less than 163 years old. Wistman's Wood is, in fact, the last vestige of the great Forest of Dartmoor, which once enjoyed a much more benevolent climate than the region does at present. Massive oak logs found deep in the surrounding bogs testify to the fact that trees here used to grow to normal size. Local folklore asserts that this creepy place, which looks as though it could well be haunted, is a suitable spot for hearing the wild cries of the Yeth Hounds, or Hounds of Hell, hunting human souls on wild autumn nights.

An oak remarkable for the opposite reason was the Duke's Walking-stick, on the Welbeck Estate in Nottinghamshire, which had a completely straight trunk towering to a height of 70 feet before producing a single branch. It had an unusually small head.

A word about the sizes of some distinguished oaks.

The largest surviving oak in Sherwood Forest, the Major Oak, has a trunk circumference of 30 feet and a height of 60 feet. It is held to be over a thousand years old and is hollow, though well supported by props and stays. The Greendale Oak, in the same area, achieved some celebrity or notoriety in the early eighteenth century by having a coach and six horses driven through a corridor cut in its trunk, though the surgery did the tree no good. The circumference of the tree above this archway, the top of which was 10 feet 3 inches above ground, was 35 feet 3 inches. The Salcey Oak, at Hartwell on the borders of Northamptonshire and Buckinghamshire, also possessed an archway but a natural one, caused by the hollowing of the tree's interior. The hollow bole was used as a stable for a horse. This tree had a bole circumference of 47 feet.

The Fairlop Oak in Hainault Forest, Essex, which ended its life of probably a thousand years or so in 1820, had a girth, three feet above ground, of 36 feet. It was most celebrated, however, for the span of its mighty branches, which shaded an area 300 feet in circumference, some of them measuring twelve inches in girth at their junction with the trunk. It was under this tree that for nearly a hundred years Fairlop Fair was held. The originator of the fair was Daniel Day, an eccentric, who formed the custom of entertaining an increasing host of friends and hangers-on to a barbecue on the first Friday of every July.

The Quiddenham or Winfarthing Oak, standing near Diss, Norfolk, when measured in 1820 was 40 feet in girth at shoulder height and 70 feet at its base. It was thought to be at least 1,300 years old and was said to have been known as the Old Oak at the time of the Norman Conquest. Hollow, as such ancient oaks usually are, its interior was once used for meetings. Its long life finally ended in 1956.

The Great Oak near Eardisley, Herefordshire, which is 30 feet 4 inches in circumference five feet above ground, gives its name to the village of Great Oak. Another huge old hollow oak in Wedgnock Park, Warwickshire, had a girth of 40 feet one foot above ground. It was once the favourite shelter of a lively bull who effectively kept visitors out of the adjacent pasture. An oak in Melbury Park, west Dorset, bearing the unexplained name of Billy Wilkins, measured 35 feet in circumference five feet above ground early this century.

These figures show that the measurements of the Chetham Oak, which is approximately 70 feet high, has a canopy spread of 300 feet in diameter and a trunk circumference of some 35 feet five feet above ground, are about average for an oak eight hundred or so years old.

To form a rough estimate of the age of a tree, allow one year

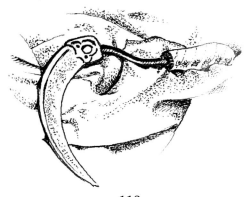

for every inch of trunk circumference. This is for trees in open country; for trees in woodlands allow two years for every inch. The circumference should be measured at five feet above the ground. Taking account of the fact that the Chetham Oak grew in a wood and so applying the second yardstick, our tree should be 840 years old. But one imagines that for such a patriarch growth will have been slower in the past few centuries, so it might well be older.

7

OAK TIMBER

FOREST FIRE is a hazard the Chetham Oak has escaped perhaps four or five times in its long life, but danger from man has, until this century, been an ever-present menace. From its sapling phase in early Norman times through every century to the present the great oak has seen its contemporaries claimed by axe and saw.

Imaginative pictures of early American settlements depict the settlers' huts as log cabins, but this is a mistake. There was no tradition in England of building in that fashion. The Pilgrim Fathers would not have known how to set about constructing a log cabin. The standard English village house, of the sort they dwelt in in their homeland, was timber-framed with infilling, usually of wattle hurdles well plastered.

For the timber frame beams of considerable size and strength were needed, and the favourite wood for the purpose was oak. One of the simplest and earliest types of frame was the cruck frame, which displays a triangular gabled end, the roof extending right to the ground. The pattern may have derived from an up-ended boat. A boatload of settlers arriving in Britain from across the North Sea would turn their boat upside down and convert it into a house.

This might suggest that the use of timber for boats preceded that of timber for houses, but probably the two were contemporaneous. Back in the earliest times a hollow tree would have served quite satisfactorily as a house, and sitting astride a floating log was an effective primitive method of crossing a river. Certainly there is evidence that as early as Neolithic times, say by 3500 BC, there were plenty of accomplished seafarers. By that date Britain had become an island, so invaders and colonisers had to come by sea. And, somewhat surprisingly, it seems that many of them did not take the shortest route across the Straits of Dover but made the Dorset, Devon and Cornish coasts their landfall, perhaps voyaging direct from Iberia.

For such voyages rafts would have been quite inadequate. Coracles, constructed of skins stretched over a timber frame, which are still in use on Welsh and Border county rivers, are considered by some authorities to be miniature examples of larger seagoing vessels of prehistoric ages. By Celtic times, in the first millennium BC, big timber ships were probably quite as common on the seas of north-western Europe as in the Mediterranean. After all, in the great sea battle off the coast of Britanny in 56 BC the Roman fleet and that of the Veneti, a Celtic nation, had met on more or less equal terms, victory going to the Romans only because an untimely calm prevented their opponents' ships from exercising their superior manoeuvrability. An excavated Roman warship of that period is 230 feet long, has a beam of 110 feet, and is constructed of wooden planks pinned

113

together and to the hull. The Celtic ships were probably similar.

Other evidence exists that from Neolithic times onwards the people of Britain were well accustomed to handling massive timbers. The great stones of Stonehenge, the biggest of which weighs 50 tons, were dragged into place, over a course of at least two miles, on mighty rollers which must have been fashioned from huge tree-trunks, probably oak. The lake villages of Meare and Godney, in the Somerset lowlands near Glastonbury, were built, probably in about 250 BC, on artificial islands constructed on colossal timbers fastened to great piles driven into the lake bed. They were approached by way of a timber causeway, protected by a drawbridge.

The elegant long-ships of the Vikings were built to an advanced and sophisticated design, besides being extremely strong and seaworthy. The celebrated Gokstad ship, built in Norway about the year 850, has as its keel a straight-grained oak trunk 80 feet long. Thick oak planks are scarfed together, with trenails (pins of hardwood) used for fastenings. These planks were fashioned from wedge-shaped timbers produced by cleaving a log into 32 equal sections, cleft wood being stronger than sawn. As a matter of fact, it seems that early and indeed later carpenters much preferred axes and adzes to saws.

By Nelson's time it took a thousand mature oaks to build a ship of the line. In fact, for the largest vessels two thousand or three thousand were needed, and it was said that 80 acres of oaks had to be felled to provide timbers for the *Victory*. One of the greatest demands was for curved timbers, to fit into the curved lines of the ship. These were normally taken from the junction of the trunk with a massive branch. A particularly difficult timber to find was a wing transom, for which an oak had to produce, instead of a tall central trunk, two approximately equal limbs forking from a short trunk. Some master shipbuilders, notably the celebrated Phineas Pett, used to make extensive expeditions to the forests to choose his timbers from growing trees. As a rule, oaks with straight trunks were found in woodlands, where they had to grow tall to compete with their neighbours, while angled timbers were produced by isolated or hedgerow trees.

During the Napoleonic Wars the oak was naturally linked with the patriotic fervour which greeted Nelson's victories. 'Hearts of oak are our ships,' sang the rejoicing citizens, as the news of each fresh triumph circulated. And patriotic landowners vied with each other in making new plantations of oaks to replace the wastage of war. As late as 1826 William Cobbett on one of his rural rides observed:

> I perceive that they are planting oaks on the 'wastes' . . . which is very good. . . . In time the oaks arrive at timber state and add to the beauty and the real wealth of the descendants of the planter, who in every such case merits unequivocal praise because he plants for his children's children.

That is always true, but long before the end of his century the oaken ships of which Cobbett was thinking had been rendered obsolete by iron ships driven by steam. He was in distinguished company in being unable to foresee such a development. If Napoleon had been a little more receptive of new ideas he might well have won the war against England. In 1803, when he was planning to invade England from Boulogne, an American engineer came to him with a plan to defeat the English navy by the use of steam-powered ships. Napoleon dismissed him brusquely: 'What, sir, you would make a ship sail against the wind and currents by lighting a bonfire under her decks? I pray you excuse me. I have no time to listen to such nonsense.'

As the old 'wooden walls of England' were replaced by ironclads their timbers became available for buildings on land. This was the traditional fate of ships' timbers. Wood from the Pilgrim Fathers' ship, the *Mayflower*, for instance, survives today as part of a great barn at Jordans, Buckinghamshire. Now the supply was greatly increased, but the demand was equal to it. Oak timbers from ships of Nelson's day are still to be seen in many Victorian barns. The tall straight timbers served well as upright king-posts, supporting the weight of the roof and usually set on piers of brick or stone so that their base should not be in contact with the damp floor. Parallel rows of king-posts at regular intervals extended the length of the barn and carried horizontal beams to bear the weight of the rafters. Curved timbers were particularly valued as supports for the roof or to help hold the king-posts steady. The timbers used in barns are, as a rule, crudely hewn and shaped by an adze. They are fitted together with mortices and tenons and fastened by oak pins, not nails. Mortice slots observable in places where they serve no useful purpose reveal that the timbers were once used elsewhere, most likely in ships. Much more elegant and meticulously planed and finished are the timbers specifically cut and shaped for roofs more important than those of barns. Finest of all are probably the hammer-beam roofs, which reached their peak of perfection in the late Middle Ages. Hammer-beams are short horizontal beams which project from the wall posts and support the main arch. Their effect is to narrow the space to be spanned and so enable the roof to be taken to greater heights than would otherwise be possible. Westminster Hall provides a splendid and well-known example.

When the first English settlements took root in the forests timber was the natural building material for ecclesiastical as well as domestic buildings, but most of the ancient wooden churches have long ago been replaced by stone. The oldest timber church in England, at Greensted in Essex, dates from about AD 825. Its walls are of split oak logs set vertically and secured by wooden fastenings. Close examination has suggested that all the logs were cleft from one tree-trunk, an enormous oak at least 600 years old when it was felled.

Many churches which now appear to be entirely of stone are sturdily reinforced by internal timbers. Huge timbers used as scaffolding in the building of Salisbury Cathedral were never taken down but were incorporated into the fabric of the tower, to which they gave increased strength. The famous crooked spire of Chesterfield is thought to owe its twist to the use of green or unseasoned oak timber in its frame, such wood being liable to warp. Incidentally, Salisbury Cathedral was formerly roofed with oak shingles.

Much of the splendid oak panelling of which the late Middle Ages and Tudor times provide so many examples suggests the pattern of upright split logs noted in the walls of Greensted church and may have evolved from it. Other patterns of panelling of the same period, just as aesthetically attractive to us, are plainer and were little regarded by our

117

ancestors, who covered them with tapestry and textiles whenever possible. For all types of panelling, however, oak was the most popular wood. Before glass came into general use for windows the window spaces were often filled with 'fine rifts of oak, lattice-wise'.

Indeed, in an Elizabethan hall most of the interior walls and the furniture would be of oak. Prominent would be a massive old oak chest, heritage of an earlier age when furniture of any kind was scarce. The older it was, the rougher and heavier. Panelled chests, which became quite common in the latter part of the sixteenth century, were beautifully planed and finished and had patterns carved on frame and panels, but those earlier examples were nearly all rough-hewn. They were used for storing all manner of goods, and they also served as stools and tables, even beds if they were long enough. Some churches still possess medieval oak chests in which they keep parish registers and other local treasures.

In the Elizabethan manor-house massive wooden tables, now as smooth as a plane could make them but still of oak, replaced the more primitive refectory tables of earlier times. For seating around them carved oak stools were now being provided, while on the table most of the bowls, platters, drinking vessels, salt cellars and even spoons and ladles were also fashioned of oak. Panelled oak cupboards lined the walls.

In the kitchen were yet more examples of the woodworker's craft. Here were barrels, buckets, wash-tubs, jugs, pitchers and, of course, more benches and stools. For casks and barrels

oak was especially important, for several alcoholic drinks, notably sherry, brandy and whisky, need oak to develop their characteristic bouquets and flavours. And only seasoned cleft oak will do.

The late Middle Ages had witnessed a revival in the use of the pole lathe, and by Elizabeth I's reign skilled wood-turners were becoming increasingly numerous and versatile. The status of the wood-carver was improving. A few centuries earlier he had been regarded as very much inferior to the stonemason, whose work he tried to emulate, expecting that his own work, if of high enough quality, would be painted over to look like stonework. Now it was becoming evident that the exquisite tracery he had shown himself capable of producing on rood-screens, choir stalls, misericords, bench-ends and other items of church furnishing was superior in some respects to stone. Wood and stone each had its place.

After the Reformation in England wood-carvers found themselves with a different set of patrons and customers. The change coincided with a general increase in prosperity, and the new-rich demanded a greater degree of comfort and luxury than had contented their fathers. Before that time few stools and benches had backs, for instance, but now the demand was for chairs designed for comfort. Chair-making was largely a cottage industry, or, to be more precise, a woodland industry, in the hands of independent craftsmen, known as 'bodgers', who worked either singly or in pairs. At first the traditional oak was used, but later beech was found to be perhaps more suitable for the legs and backs of chairs, set into seats of elm.

From the earliest times oak timbers have been in common use on the farm. The employment of great oak trunks as rollers for conveying the enormous stones of Stonehenge, Avebury and other prehistoric monuments to their sites has already been mentioned. In all probability the wheel was developed from the obvious device of slicing off a section of such a trunk. Early cart-wheels were often solid discs of timber, though sometimes comprising several sections fitted together, on a fixed axle. As lighter spoked wheels were developed it was found that certain woods were best suited to certain parts of them. Elm was best for the stock, hub or nave, this being the toughest timber available. The felloes, or sections of the rim, were always of ash, and the spokes were always of oak, cleft not sawn. Oak pegs were also used for fastening the felloe sections together.

Traditional woods were also used for the various parts of horse-drawn waggons and carts, universally employed for farm work until forty or fifty years ago. The frame was almost always of oak, the floor of elm, the sides of either ash or poplar.

Oak was extensively used in the construction of mills, both water- and wind-driven. Elm was considered the best for brake-blocks, bearings and any parts that came into contact with the water, but for the framework, drive shafts and gears oak was preferred. In old post-mills the centre post is generally of truly massive oak timbers.

Perhaps because of the experience gained by woodworkers in fashioning gears and other quite intricate parts of machinery in mills and elsewhere, and also because the lubricants now used were not then available, wood was employed in some of the earliest clocks.

Oak Timber

Some clocks were made entirely of wood, particularly in early nineteenth-century America, where wooden clocks became the subject of an early experiment in mass production.

The earliest machines which heralded the Industrial Revolution were also of wood, though iron and steel soon took over. The first spinning machines were of wood; so were the first railway waggons, as well as the rails on which they ran. Wooden rails remained in common use in America until the 1870s, though they had a life of only a few months. Most of the bridges on the railways which opened up the west of America and Canada were constructed of timber. Wooden coal waggons, with heavy oak frames, were widely used long before they were moved along their rails by steam power. Wooden barges carried heavy loads along canals, in which the locks were constructed of great baulks of timber. The frames of some old lock gates are of mighty oak beams at least one foot square.

I have already mentioned the use of oak bark for tanning leather. Oak bark, especially the inner layers of bark on young trees, is rich in tannin. It can be peeled off only in spring, when the sap is rising, and has to be set out to dry while keeping the tannin-rich inner bark protected from rain – a tricky problem. Today the trees are usually felled first and the bark stripped off afterwards, but in the Forest of Dean old-time woodmen developed the custom of stripping the bark off quite large trees while they were standing and then allowing them to remain erect until the following winter. There was a belief that winter-felled oak was better than that cut at other seasons.

In addition to its use for tanning leather, the tannin from oak bark, when mixed with salts of iron, makes good writing ink. Mixed with alum it produces an excellent brown dye, while mixtures with other salts give dyes of yellow, black and purple.

Oak bark was even used medically, though its efficacy depended more on magic than on any other qualities. Here is a typical recipe:

> Against dysentery. Take half a poor cheese, not greasy, add four slices of English honey, boil in a pan until brown. Then take a handful of bark of young oak and bring it home in silence and never into the house of the patient. Scrape off the green outside. Boil the juicy chips in cow milk, sweeten the drink with three slices of honey, then take it with cheese. After the drink you must abstain from ale for seven days and you must drink milk that has not turned sour. (Cockayne, 1864)

Oak for building houses and churches, oak for ships, oak for tools and furniture, oak for carts and waggons, oak for utensils, oak for casks and barrels, oak for fencing, oak for tanning leather, oak for ink, oak for healing the sick – how could our ancestors have managed without oak?

The men of Old England had at least as good a claim as the ancient Druids to be called the men of the oak.

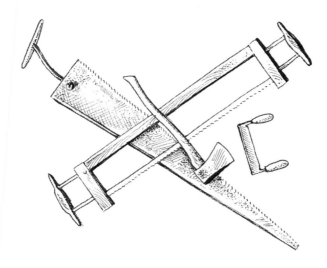

8

THE OAK IN DECAY

As LONG as England stands, the great Oak of Chetham is safe from axe and saw. Its iron-hard heartwood will never be cleft or sawn. As a monument inherited from the distant and ever-receding past, it will live out its natural span of life, of which it is at present only in the late afternoon. Eight hundred years is late middle age, no more. With the danger from human interference removed, it could well last another four or five hundred years.

Inexorably, of course, time will take its toll and old age creep up on it. The seeds of its dissolution are already sown. That bolt of lightning which seared its trunk at an unrecorded date penetrated its defences and admitted the forces of decay. As each family of bird occupants move, after their spring nesting, out of the sheltering hollow in the bole, insects, mites and the hosts of micro-organisms busy themselves with the processing of the droppings and debris left behind. Rain seeps in. Then frost causes the droplets of moisture to expand and force new cracks in the surrounding wood. Each year the hole grows larger.

Each year mosses creep farther up the trunk of the oak. Each year the polypody ferns edge farther along the great limbs. Each year wood-boring larvae of moths, beetles and wood-wasps eat deeper tunnels into the dead branches, and each year the woodpeckers press ahead with their demolition programme in attempts to get at them. An elderberry seed voided by a starling is starting to grow in a crack in the bark a few inches from the little owl's hole. If unchecked its rapidly growing roots will probe beneath the dead bark, eventually peeling it off and exposing the heartwood and the next sector of living bark to attack. Quite possibly Jim Noyce will notice the danger and remove the intruding seedling, but if so he will only be postponing the inevitable. Sooner or later other seedlings will take root in the living body of the old oak.

We can visualise the oak in its old age. The nesting hole has become a hollow occupying the entire middle of the bole. The agents of disintegration have eaten away the unprotected heartwood until the hollow is big enough to shelter a man. But the outer layers of the trunk are still living. There the oak's hydraulic system pursues its annual rhythm, carrying water and mineral nutrients each spring from rootlets to twigs, as it has done for, by this time, over a thousand years. So each spring the miracle of rising sap produces its effusion of foliage

and flowers, to be succeeded each autumn by a crop of acorns. If every other acorn it has produced in its long life perished, the old oak could still supply its successor. It is receiving assistance. As a senior citizen of the realm it is entitled to some support. Thick iron hoops have been placed around it to prevent the shell of the trunk from splitting. Huge props, themselves the trunks of lesser trees, help to carry the weight of the sagging horizontal limbs. There is talk of filling the entire hollow with concrete, as a dentist fills a hollow tooth.

Some successful operations to prolong the lives of old oaks have already been referred to. The Great Oak in the hamlet of that name in Herefordshire has been successfully treated by tree surgeons in recent years. The Carmarthen Oak, though dead, has its shell filled with concrete and is protected by railings so that it can never fall down and so doom the town. Kett's Oak, a vestige of an oak near Wymondham, Norfolk, and now with a girth nearly equal to its height, has within the past hundred years been banded with iron, filled with concrete and bitumen, sprayed against caterpillars, mulched with sulphate of potash, subjected to sundry other indignities and finally fenced with railings – to some effect, it seems, for it is still alive. The Major Oak, reputedly the oldest and largest surviving tree in Sherwood Forest, is hollow, has shrunk with age and needs the support of iron props and braces, but it too manages to flourish.

Perhaps by the time the Chetham Oak approaches the point of collapse, several centuries hence, new techniques will be available to prolong its life still further. Of course, even they would not be able to do so indefinitely. When eventually, after a long and eventful life, the last scraps of the Fairlop Oak were demolished by a gale a builder rescued some of the still sound wood and fashioned it into a pulpit and reading desk still to be seen in a church in St Pancras. Maybe some similar fate awaits the Chetham Oak.

On a tranquil spring evening Jim Noyce is standing beneath the tree. Here, in a point of time, his life impinges on the life of every other member of the teeming commonwealth of the oak. He measures his own life in years, allowing himself seventy or eighty of them. He watches a brimstone butterfly,

recently emerged from hibernation with perhaps two months of life ahead of it. A willow-warbler, delighted to be safely back from Africa, looks forward to a full nesting season, probably its last. The sow badger, waiting in her sett beneath the oak for him to depart so that she can bring her cubs out for exercise and play, has already produced her replacement for the future. The primroses, the bracken and the lichen on the oak bark may well live as long as the oak itself. A gnat snatched up by the willow-warbler has ended its brief life only marginally earlier than if it had lived out its normal span.

So it was a thousand years ago, when a Noyce of another

generation stood beneath another tree, the parent of our oak, and saw the brimstone butterfly and the primroses and heard the willow-warbler's cascading song. So it will be a thousand years hence, when a future Noyce, a remote descendant of Jim, will see the same sights, breathe in the same woodland scents, appreciate the same birdsong, while standing under another though very similar oak.

The thousand or so years of the life of the oak are as finite as the minutes of the life of the bacteria whose role is to recycle all its immense bulk. Nothing is immortal. Yet perhaps the oak, with its multitudinous and ever-renewing population of living creatures, comes as near to that state as anything can.

APPENDIX

The oak is a bountiful tree acting as host to a multitude of plants and animals at any one time. Most of those that have been mentioned in earlier pages are listed here. This is not intended to be a definitive list for many other species will seek shelter or even feed on the oak in passing, but it nevertheless gives some indication of the size of the tree's close-knit family.

Where possible I have given English names.

MAMMALS

Hedgehog	Dormouse
Mole	Bank Vole
Shrew	Short-tailed Vole
Greater Horseshoe Bat	Common Vole
Lesser Horseshoe Bat	Harvest Mouse
Daubenton's Bat	Long-tailed Field Mouse
Whiskered Bat	Yellow-necked Mouse
Natterer's Bat	House Mouse
Long-eared Bat	Brown Rat
Barbastelle	Fox
Pipistrelle	Badger
Serotine	Stoat
Noctule	Weasel
Rabbit	Fallow Deer
Hare	Roe Deer
Grey Squirrel	Chinese Water Deer

BIRDS

Buzzard	Blackcap
Sparrow-hawk	Whitethroat
Kestrel	Lesser Whitethroat
Hobby	Willow-Warbler
Pheasant	Chiffchaff
Woodcock	Wood-Warbler
Wood-Pigeon	Goldcrest

Stock Dove
Collared Dove
Turtle Dove
Cuckoo
Little Owl
Long-eared Owl
Tawny Owl
Barn Owl
Nightjar
Great Spotted Woodpecker
Lesser Spotted Woodpecker
Green Woodpecker
Swallow
House Martin
Swift
Tree Pipit
Pied Wagtail
Red-backed Shrike
Starling
Jay
Magpie
Jackdaw
Rook
Carrion Crow
Hedge Sparrow
Grasshopper Warbler
Garden Warbler

Spotted Flycatcher
Pied Flycatcher
Redstart
Robin
Nightingale
Blackbird
Song-Thrush
Mistle-Thrush
Fieldfare
Redwing
Marsh Tit
Willow Tit
Blue Tit
Great Tit
Coal Tit
Long-tailed Tit
Nuthatch
Tree-Creeper
House Sparrow
Chaffinch
Brambling
Bullfinch
Greenfinch
Goldfinch
Linnet
Lesser Redpoll
Yellowhammer

BUTTERFLIES UNDER AND AROUND THE OAK

Large White
Small White
Green-veined White
Wood White
Orange-tip
Clouded Yellow
Brimstone
White Admiral
Purple Emperor
Comma
Small Tortoiseshell
Peacock

Small Pearl-bordered
   Fritillary
Marbled White
Ringlet
Grayling
Speckled Wood
Wall
Meadow Brown
Gatekeeper
Small Heath
Purple Hairstreak
Small Copper

Red Admiral
Painted Lady
Silver-washed Fritillary
High Brown Fritillary
Pearl-bordered
  Fritillary

Common Blue
Small Blue
Holly Blue
Small Skipper
Essex Skipper
Large Skipper

BUTTERFLY CATERPILLARS FEEDING ON THE OAK

The following is the only species:
Purple Hairstreak

MOTH CATERPILLARS FEEDING ON THE OAK

Blotched Emerald
False Mocha
Maiden's Blush
Birch Mocha
Winter Moth
Broken-barred Carpet
Red Green Carpet
Autumn Green Carpet
November Moth
Marbled Pug
Brindled Pug
Oak-tree Moth
August Thorn
Canary-shouldered Thorn
September Thorn
Lunar Thorn
Purple Thorn
Scalloped Hazel
Feathered Thorn
Swallow-tailed Moth
Scorched Wing
Early Moth
Spring Usher
Scarce Umber
Dotted Border
Mottled Umber
March Moth
Pale Brindled Beauty
Small Brindled Beauty
Oak Beauty
Peppered Moth
Satin Carpet
Great Oak Beauty
Pale Oak Beauty
Engrailed
Little Emerald
Light Emerald
Brindled White-spot
Square Spot
Festoon

Yellow-tail
Gipsy Moth
Black Arches
Lackey
Pale Oak Eggar
December Moth
Pebble Hook-tip
Scarce Hook-tip
Oak Hook-tip
Small Black Arches
Least Black Arches
Green Silver-lines
Scarce Silver-lines
Large Marbled Tortrix
Common Emerald
Scarce Merveille du Jour
Nut-tree Tussock
Sycamore
Alder
Scarce Dagger
Grey Arches
Cabbage Moth
Beautiful Brocade
Brindled Green
Sprawler
Merveille du Jour
Copper Underwing
Hebrew Character
Blossom Underwing
Small Quaker
Common Quaker
Clouded Drab
Twin-spotted Quaker
Heart Moth
Lunar-spotted Pinion
Angle-striped Sallow
Dun-bar
Yellow-line Quaker
Flounced Chestnut
Brown-spot Pinion

Triangle
Lobster Moth
Marbled Brown
Lunar Marbled Brown
Great Prominent
Coxcomb Prominent
Lesser Satin
Lesser Lutestring
Frosted Green
Vapourer
Scarce Vapourer
Pale Tussock

Orange Underwing
Chestnut
Dark Chestnut
Dotted Chestnut
Satellite
Tawny Pinion
Pale Pinion
Grey Shoulder-knot
Lunar Double-stripe
Dark Crimson Underwing
Light Crimson Underwing

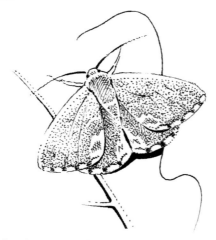

The following species feed on lichens growing on the oak:

Red-necked Footman
Rosy Footman
Four-dotted Footman
Four-spotted Footman

Buff Footman
Common Footman
Orange Footman
Dotted Carpet

The following species feed on the wood of the oak:
Goat Moth
Leopard Moth

The following species feeds on the underside of the bark of the oak:
Yellow-legged Clearwing

The following species feeds on the dead leaves of the oak:
Common Fanfoot

133

MICRO-MOTHS (PYRALID AND PLUME MOTHS) ASSOCIATED WITH THE OAK

(* indicates that the caterpillar feeds on the oak)

Crambus pinellus
*Phycita spissicella**
*Acrobasis tumidella**
*Acrobasis tumidana**
*Acrobasis consociella**
*Cryptoblabes bistriga**
*Endrotricha flammealis**
Scoparia ulmella
Scoparia ambigualis
Scoparia basistrigalis
Scoparia centurionalis
Scoparia mercuria
Scoparia truncicolella
Sylepta ruralis (Mother-o'-Pearl Moth)

Perinephela lancealis
Eurrhypara hortulata (Small Magpie Moth)
Pyrausta fuscalis
Pyrausta purpuralis
Pyrausta pandalis
Amblyptilia punctidactyla
Amblyptilia acanthodactyla
Stenoptilia bipunctidactyla
Stenoptilia pterodactyla
Alucita galactodactyla
Leioptilus osteodactylus
Leioptilus tephradactylus
Orneodes hexadactyla

BEETLES ASSOCIATED WITH THE OAK

Carabus violaceus (Violet Ground-beetle)
Carabus nemoralis
Leistus spinibarbis
Anchomenus angusticollis
Lathrobium elongatum
Lathrobium fulvipenne
Trogosita mauritanica
Ditoma crenata
Mycetophagus quadripustulatus
Typhaea fumata
Lucanus cervus (Stag Beetle)
Melolontha vulgaris (Cockchafer)
Rhizotrogus solstitialis
Cetonia aurata (Rose-chafer)
Trixagus dermestoides
Melanotus castanipes
Lampyris noctiluca (Glow-worm)

Lymexylon navale
Anobium tesselatum
Tenebrio molitor (Mealworm Beetle)
Pytho depressus
Orchesia micans
Melandrya caraboides
Pyrochroa rubens
Meloe proscaraboeus (Oil Beetle)
Phyllobius calcartus
Orchestes quercus
Magdalinus pruni
Attelabus curculionoides
Rhyncites pubescens
Clytus arietis
Rhagium inquisitor
Endomychus coccineus
Coccinella bipunctata (Two-spot Ladybird)
Coccinella septempunctata

Malthinus marginatus
Malthinus sanguinolentus
Tillus elongatus
Opilus mollis
Clerus formicarius

Corynetes caeruleus
  (Seven-spot Ladybird)
Coccinella decempunctata
  (Ten-spot Ladybird)
Coccinella duodecimguttata
  (Twelve-spot Ladybird)

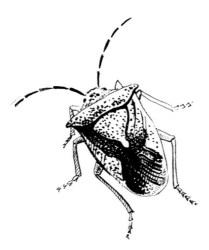

SPIDERS OF THE OAK

Harpacta hombergi
Oonops pulcher
Micrommata viridissimma
Clubiona corticalis
Clubiona compta
Agroeca brunnea
Agroeca proxima
Salticus cingulatus
Dictyna uncinata
Dictyna arundinacea
Dictyna latens

Dictyna viridissimma
Tegenaria silvestris
Lycosa saccata
Lycosa lugubris
Trochosa terricola
Trochosa ruricola
Theridion lunatum
Episinus truncatus
Drapetisca socialis
Aranea cucurbitina

HYMENOPTERA (BEES, WASPS AND ANTS) ASSOCIATED WITH THE OAK

Hornet
Tree Wasp
Wood-borer Wasp
Wood-carving Leafcutter
  Bee
Red Osmia
Fringed Osmia
Blue Osmia
Wood-carder Bee
Wood Ant
Narrow-headed Ant
Goat Moth Ichneumon-fly

Oak-apple Gall-fly
Marble Gall-fly
Currant Gall-fly
Spangle Gall-fly
Silk Button Gall-fly
Cherry Gall-fly
Hop Gall-fly
Buff-tailed Bumble-bee
Early Bumble-bee
Eriocampa annulipes (larva
  of this Saw-fly feeds on
  oak leaves)

PLANT BUGS (HEMIPTERA) OF THE OAK

(* denotes eggs laid and larvae feeding on some part of the oak)

Aradus depressus
Aneurus laevis
*Aneurus avenius**
*Acanthsoma haemorrhoidiale**
*Pentatoma rufipes**
*Troilus luridus**
Drymus brunneus
Scolopostethus thomsoni
Acalypta brunnea
Acalypta carinata
Acalypta platychila
*Himacerus apterus**
Temnostethus gracilis
Temnostethus pusillus
*Anthocoris confusus**
*Anthocoris nemoralis**
*Anthocoris nemorum**
Xylocoris cursitans
Dufouriellus ater
Loricula elegantula
*Deraeocoris lutescens**
*Harpocera thoracica**

*Phylus melanocephalus**
*Psallus perrisi**
*Psallus wagneri**
*Psallus quercus**
Psallus diminutus
Psallus varians
Campyloneura virgula
*Cyllecoris histrionicus**
*Dryophilocoris flavoquadrima-
  culatus**
*Orthotylus tenellus**
*Orthotylus nassatus**
*Orthotylus prasinus**
*Lygocoris viridis**
*Miris striatus**
*Calocoris quadripunctatus**
*Megacoelum infusum**
*Phytocoris tiliae**
*Phytocoris populi**
*Phytocoris dimidiatus**
*Phytocoris longipennis**
*Phytocoris reuteri**

FLOWERS UNDER AND AROUND THE CHETHAM OAK

Wood Anemone	Primrose
Columbine	Cowslip
Traveller's Joy	Creeping Jenny
Flixweed	Centaury
Cuckoo-flower	Vervain
Garlic Mustard	Field Bindweed
Shepherd's Purse	Hedge Bindweed
Wild Mignonette	Woody Nightshade
Weld	Great Mullein
Milkwort	Dark Mullein
Rock-rose	Figwort
Fairy Flax	Foxglove
St John's-wort	Germander Speedwell
Dog Violet	Wood Speedwell
Sweet Violet	Thyme-leaved Speedwell
Wild Pansy	Cow-wheat
White Campion	Eyebright
Bladder Campion	Yellow Rattle
Chickweed	Pennyroyal
Greater Stitchwort	Red Deadnettle
Mouse-ear	White Deadnettle
Fat-hen	Yellow Archangel
Mallow	Wild Basil
Musk Mallow	Basil Thyme
Herb Robert	Marjoram
Long-stalked Cranesbill	Ground Ivy
Dovesfoot Cranesbill	Hedge Woundwort
Rest-harrow	Black Horehound
Red Clover	Selfheal
Zigzag Clover	Bugle
White Clover	Wood Sage
Alsike Clover	Wood Forget-me-not
Hop Trefoil	Gromwell
Lesser Trefoil	Ribwort Plantain
Tufted Vetch	Hoary Plantain
Bush Vetch	Nettle-leaved Bellflower
Vetch	Harebell
Yellow Vetch	Elder
Wood Vetch	Guelder Rose

Hairy Vetchling
Black Medick
Birdsfoot Trefoil
Horseshoe Vetch
Kidney Vetch
Sainfoin
Blackthorn
Wild Cherry
Dog Rose
Bramble
Wild Raspberry
Dewberry
Tormentil
Creeping Cinquefoil
Silverweed
Barren Strawberry
Wild Strawberry
Agrimony
Salad Burnet
Wood Avens
Orpine
Rosebay Willowherb
Enchanter's Nightshade
Broad-leaved Willowherb
Dog's Mercury
Annual Mercury
Nettle
White Bryony
Spurge Laurel
Holly
Ivy
Dogwood
Buckthorn
Spindle
Hazel
Sallow
Wood Spurge
Fool's Parsley
Cow Parsley
Hogwood
Burnet Saxifrage
Wood Sanicle

Honeysuckle
Wayfaring Tree
Valerian
Moschatel
Hedge Bedstraw
Lady's Bedstraw
Goosegrass
Woodruff
Squinancy-wort
Field Madder
Teasel
Small Scabious
Field Scabious
Devilsbit Scabious
Groundsel
Ox-eye Daisy
Daisy
Yarrow
Hemp Agrimony
Mugwort
Spear Thistle
Marsh Thistle
Musk Thistle
Creeping Thistle
Black Knapweed
Greater Knapweed
Burdock
Cotton Thistle
Dandelion
Wild Lettuce
Catsear
Rough Hawkbit
Nipplewort
Smooth Hawksbeard
Mouse-ear Hawkweed
Smooth Sow-thistle
Solomon's Seal
Lily-of-the-Valley
Bluebell
Ramsons
Stinking Iris
Cuckoo-pint

Wood Dock
Broad-leaved Dock
Curled Dock
Sorrel
Knotgrass

Broad-leaved Helleborine
Twayblade
Early Purple Orchid
Greater Butterfly Orchid
Lesser Butterfly Orchid
Spotted Orchid
Fragrant Orchid

FERNS FOUND UNDER, AROUND AND ON THE OAK

Bracken
Hard Fern
Lady Fern
Prickly Shield Fern
Male Fern

Prickly Buckler Fern
Broad Buckler Fern
Polypody
Royal Fern
Adder's Tongue

SOME LICHENS OF THE OAK

Parmelia amplissimma
Parmelia pulverulenta
Parmelia stellaris
Parmelia ceratophylla
Parmelia parietina
Usnea barbata (Beard Moss)
Ramalina farinacea
Cetrari glauca
Peltigera canina
Sticta pulmonaris (Lungs of the Oak)
Lecanora atra
Lecanora subfusca
Lecanora pallescens
Lecanora varia
Urceolaria cinereus

Lecidea punctata
Lecidea sanguinaria
Lecidea sphaeroides
Opegrapha varia
Opegrapha atra
Opegrapha vulgata
Graphis scripta
Chiographa lyellii
Lecanactis lyncea
Arthonia astroidea
Coniocarpon cinnabarinum
Pertusaria communis
Calicium chrysocephalum
Coniocybe furfuracea
Sagedia aggregata
Verrucaria epidermidis